Il-Mejda Għawdxija
THE GOZO TABLE

Recipes from a Mediterranean Island
George Borg

Compiled and edited by: Hilda Maguire and Colm Regan

Photography by: Claire Borg *(with Tony Daly, Dylan Creane, Ciara Regan, George Scicluna and Joe Spiteri)*

Design by: Dylan Creane

Published by Gallerija Press, Gozo, 2012

For Stephanie, Margherita and Andrea

Editors' Note

We have put together Il-Mejda Għawdxija - the Gozo Table to celebrate much that is great about Gozitan food and wine and to highlight its quality and versatility. Inevitably we have had to leave out more than we could put in – produce and producers, recipes and styles, places and people – it would simply have been impossible to include it all in this short book. For this, we apologise in advance. In this sense Il-Mejda Għawdxija does not claim to be comprehensive in any way – it is simply an introduction.

We have also included a brief introduction to some of the wines and wine makers of Gozo because of the importance of the 'revolution' that is currently taking place in the industry and because of its intrinsic link to the Gozo table. Again, this is simply an introduction and is, in no way, comprehensive.

In the recipes, we have stayed true to local methods and traditions as far as possible – for example, we have extensively used sheep's cheese (fresh and peppered) as this is what is used locally; however, you can readily substitute mozzarella, ricotta, feta or similar cheeses in most of the recipes – the taste and texture may be slightly different but the overall result will be much the same. The essential principle of the recipe's and the methods used is to keep it simple and to use the best, fresh local produce as far as is possible.

Servings: the majority of dishes in this book have been designed to serve 4 people.

Gallerija Press
#6 Gallerija Court
Triq Bullara, Ix-Xaghra, Gozo

© Gallerija Press 2012 and individual contributors

ISBN 978-0-9567185-6-3

Printed and bound in Malta by Gutenberg

FSC
www.fsc.org
MIX
Paper from
responsible sources
TT-CoC-002424

TABLE OF CONTENTS

INTRODUCTION

While my father was a professional chef and I lived in a home where cooking was a way of life, it was in my mother's kitchen that I developed my interest in food and in cooking. Watching her make dishes such as sheep's cheese ravioli, pigeon broth, salted tuna and cauliflower pie made its mark on me and instilled a passion for things fresh, local and seasonal. Our table changed as the seasons changed and, as in so many cultures worldwide, certain foods became associated with certain feast days or festivals – fava beans and Kusksu in the spring, Lampuki pie with autumn etc. Today, as a professional chef I try to keep those same values and approaches alive and to renew and adapt them to changing tastes and times. For me, this is what this recipe book is all about – preserving what is best about Gozo's kitchen while, at the same time, ensuring that it does not get left in the past. For me, that is what my cooking is all about.

Rightly so, Gozo has developed a reputation for growing some of the finest produce in the Mediterranean. Visitors from Malta and abroad travel to the island expecting something local and above all, fresh. Our village squares are busy every morning with shoppers buying what is needed on a daily basis for their table – sheep's cheese in its various forms, vegetables of the highest quality, fresh local bread and the finest of tomatoes and fruit in season. Gozitans are proud of their produce and there isn't a household that does not have its favourite recipes handed down and adapted over time. Rabbit, pork, local sausage and, of course, a huge array of fish remain the staples of our cooking. Drying and/or preserving tomatoes, capers, onions and tuna as well as making tomato kunserva is something very familiar and routine in Gozitan households. This recipe book tries to simply capture some of this approach; to celebrate much of its quality and flavour while, at the same time, adding modern 'twists' and variations. Over the centuries, the surrounding Mediterranean region has had a fundamental impact on Gozo and this is significantly reflected in the way local cooking has changed over time.

As a chef, I am eager to see people of all ages learn to cook and enjoy not just the results but also the process; sitting around the table with family and friends adds something special and fundamental to our lives. Arguing about ingredients, herbs and spices not only animates our conversations but also builds the distinctive character of Gozitan cooking. However, there is always room for development and improvement and I hope some of the ideas and suggestions in this book encourage you to experiment while also retaining what is best in our tradition.

Given the quality of the ingredients we have, it is important to keep our cooking simple and uncomplicated. By doing so, the results will display that trait, its underlying flavour, its nutritional value and goodness. In the recipes that follow I have tried to reflect that simplicity by not over complicating either the ingredients or the process, but I have also included ideas that offer greater variety and diverse flavours. This, I believe will keep Gozitan cooking fresh, modern and innovative while firmly based in tried and trusted methods developed over many years.

Gozo has what is needed – tradition and experience, high quality ingredients, local knowledge and a quality table. Let's cook with enthusiasm, energy and passion!

George Borg, June 2012

Soups & Savouries
(Servings are for 4)

Soppa tat-tadam u bettieħ
TOMATO & MELON SOUP

An ideal summer soup, full of intense flavour and colour with the fresh taste of herbs and a splash of vinegar; the melon must be ripe and the tomatoes are best picked at the height of summer, however, quality tinned tomatoes with a pinch of sugar will also do the trick!

INGREDIENTS

1.5kg ripe tomatoes

2 garlic cloves

1 small onion

20ml raspberry vinegar

1 orange

½ honey dew melon

Bunch of fresh herbs (mint, basil, thyme and parsley)

Sea salt and freshly cracked pepper

200ml extra virgin olive oil

METHOD

Plunge the tomatoes in boiling water for 15 seconds, drain, cool, peel the skin, remove the seeds and roughly chop

Remove skin and seed from the melon and cut into small cubes

Lightly press the garlic leaving the skin on

Finely chop the onion and the herbs. Zest the orange and put the zest in boiling water for 5 minutes and drain

Heat a deep pan with half the oil and put in the garlic, leave to cook for 1 minute, remove and discard

Place the melon in the same pan and oil and sauté for 3 minutes, stir in the vinegar and the onion and cook for a further minute

Add the tomatoes and cook for 15 minutes, adding water if necessary

Blend the soup to a fine sauce and mix in the orange zest

Season and chill preferably overnight

Serve chilled sprinkled with olive oil and herbs.

Kisksu
BROAD BEAN & PASTA SOUP

It would be hard to imagine a recipe book without these two traditional soups, both highlighting the quality of Gozo's produce. Broad beans are used in very many dishes and are here combined with fresh sheep's cheese and pasta to make a hearty and warming meal in a bowl.

There is little more to be said about the classic tomato soup but when made with produce ripened in the Mediterranean sun and the heady scent of basil, it is simply sublime whether served hot or cold.

INGREDIENTS

2 onions, finely chopped

2 kilos fresh broad beans, skinned

300g potatoes, peeled and cut into approx. 2cm cubes

3 tablespoons tomato paste

½ teaspoon mixed spice

sea salt and freshly cracked pepper

100g kisksu pasta

50ml extra virgin olive oil

4 fresh sheep's cheese

METHOD

Heat a deep pan with the oil and shallow fry the onions until golden

Add the beans and the potatoes, stir well and add the spice and the tomato paste

Fill with approx. 1.5 litres water and simmer for 45 minutes

Stir in the pasta, cook for a further 15 minutes stirring continuously

Leave to rest for about 20 minutes before serving

To serve, heat if necessary and add the fresh cheese.

Soppa tat-tadam
TOMATO SOUP

INGREDIENTS

2kg ripe tomatoes, skinned & de-seeded

6 garlic cloves, finely chopped

1 onion, finely chopped

2 potatoes, peeled and cut into small cubes

Small bunch of fresh basil leaves, half shredded, half whole

Small bunch of parsley, finely chopped

Sea salt and freshly cracked pepper

1 slice crusty bread, cut into small pieces

200ml extra virgin olive oil

METHOD

Heat a deep pan with half the oil and sauté the garlic for 1 minute (do not let it brown)

Add the onions and sweat them until golden, then add the tomatoes and cook for 5 minutes and then the potatoes

Top up the pan with some water (just enough to cook the potatoes) and simmer for about 20 minutes or until the potatoes are cooked

Blend the soup to a fine consistency and adjust the seasoning

Heat the remaining oil in a pan and put in the bread and the whole basil leaves, toss together until golden

Heat the soup and stir in the shredded basil and parsley leaves

Serve sprinkled with the bread mixture.

Aljotta
FISH SOUP

Traditionally associated with Lent, this soup has now become a year round favourite. It is much the better when made with a good homemade stock, lots of fresh herbs, a quality tomato paste and a variety of fish fillets. If you are visiting Gozo for the first time, this is one dish on the 'must try' list – all good restaurants have it!

INGREDIENTS

For the fish stock (makes 2 litres):
5kg fish bones, preferably Grouper (clean heads and tails can also be included)
Parsley stalks
2 onions
4 tomatoes
Marjoram
5 garlic cloves
To make the stock peel the onions and garlic and roughly cut all the vegetables and place them in a pan full of water and simmer for 20 minutes, then strain and reserve.

For fish soup:
2 litres fish stock
3 onions, finely sliced
10 garlic cloves, finely sliced
4 ripe tomatoes, chopped
Bunch of marjoram, shredded
12 basil leaves, shredded
100ml extra virgin olive oil
5 tablespoons tomato paste
200g fresh mixed fish fillets cut into small cubes
Sea salt and freshly cracked pepper

For serving:
4 slices crusty bread
2 garlic cloves
Small bunch of parsley
2 lemons

METHOD

In a deep pan heat the oil and sauté the onions until golden, add the garlic and the herbs and cook for further 2 minutes, stirring continuously

Add the fish, cook for 2-3 minutes

Add the tomato paste and the tomatoes, top up with the stock

Simmer for approximately 20 minutes.

Season generally especially with the pepper

Rub the garlic clove on the crusty bread, halve the lemon and finely chop the parsley

Serve the soup with sprinkled parsley and the crusty bread together with the lemon on the side.

11

BRUSCHETTA

Gozo is well known for the quality of its bread and here it is celebrated with a range of different toppings highlighting a range of local ingredients. Easy to make and very versatile (you can design your own), they are perfect for lunch, for serving with drinks or as part of an antipasti dish.

Bit-tonn taż-żejt

TUNA PATE

INGREDIENTS

150g tuna in oil; 1tsp capers; 10g sweet tomato paste; 1 sundried tomato; a small bunch of parsley; 6 basil leaves; a few mint leaves; 75ml extra virgin olive oil; sea salt and freshly ground pepper and, to serve, a small bunch of rocket.

METHOD

Finely chop the herbs

Place all the ingredients in a bowl and with a hand blender mix to a fine paste

Season to taste and serve with fresh rocket on the side

Bil-ful u l-bejken

BROAD BEAN & BACON

INGREDIENTS

1 kg loose fresh broad beans; 100g smoked bacon; 45ml extra virgin olive oil; 1 garlic clove; sea salt and freshly cracked pepper.

METHOD

Remove the beans from the outer and inner skins

Finely chop the garlic and roughly cut the bacon

Heat a pan with the oil, add the garlic and the beans together and sauté for 2 minutes

Add the bacon and cook for a further 3 minutes

Season to taste and serve

Bigilla

WHITE BEAN PATE

INGREDIENTS

250g butter beans (preferably tinned ones as they are softer); a small bunch of parsley; 3 garlic cloves; 90 ml extra virgin olive oil; sea salt and white pepper.

METHOD

Drain the beans and mash them

Finely chop the parsley and the garlic and add it to the beans

Season to taste and add the oil

Leave to stand in the fridge for at least half an hour and serve

Ful u piżelli

BROAD BEAN & PEA

INGREDIENTS

1 kg loose fresh broad beans; 500g fresh (or frozen) peas; 3 garlic cloves; 50 ml extra virgin olive oil; sea salt and freshly cracked pepper.

METHOD

Remove the beans from the two shells and, if using fresh peas from their shell

Finely chop the garlic

Heat a pan with the oil, add the ingredients together and sauté for about 5 minutes

Season to taste and serve

Qarabagħli u nagħniegħ

COURGETTE & MINT

INGREDIENTS

300g courgette; a small bunch of fresh mint, 1garlic clove; 90 ml extra virgin olive oil; a small bunch of parsley; 15ml raspberry vinegar; sea salt and freshly cracked pepper.

METHOD

Wash and slice the courgette

Finely chop the garlic, parsley and mint

In a pan heat half the oil and sauté the courgette until still crisp

Prepare the marinade by combining garlic, mint, parsley, oil, vinegar and seasoning together

Mix the marinade with the courgette and serve

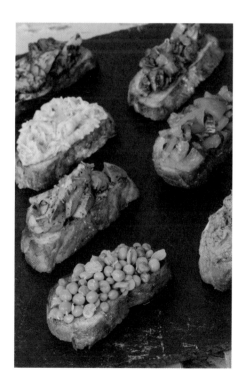

FTIRA GHAWDXIJA

Gozo's answer to pizza – a thin, easily made, and oven-baked with toppings of your choice; here we have included three. Ftira is best made in a stone oven but given that most of us do not have one, a conventional fan-assisted oven will work fine, especially if you use a pizza stone, placed low and allowed to heat up along with the oven.

Għaġina tal-ftira
FTIRA DOUGH

INGREDIENTS

500g strong plain flour
1 teaspoon fine salt
10g dried yeast
1 teaspoon sugar
1 teaspoon white pepper
3 tablespoons extra virgin olive oil
300ml lukewarm water

METHOD

In a large bowl combine, flour, salt, pepper, sugar and oil together

Dissolve yeast in the water and pour into the flour

Using a mixer or your hands knead to form a soft dough, making sure it is not sticky, continue working it for 5 minutes to give elasticity to the dough

Divide in 4 balls and let stand in the refrigerator, preferably overnight, to prove slowly and then use as needed

L-Għawdxija
GOZITAN FTIRA

INGREDIENTS

1 recipe dough
400ml extra virgin olive oil
3 potatoes, peeled and finely sliced
3 tomatoes, finely sliced
2 onions, finely sliced
6 garlic cloves, finely chopped
400g black olive, stoned and quartered
4 anchovy fillets, finely chopped
Sea salt and freshly cracked pepper
Flour for dusting

METHOD

Open the dough on a floured surface to fit a baking tray

Cover the baking tray with the dough and start placing the ingredients to fill the ftira base, starting with the tomatoes, potatoes, onions, garlic, anchovy and olives

Drizzle with olive oil, sea salt and pepper

Bake in a hot oven at 240°C for about 10 minutes until nicely browned and crispy and serve immediately.

Ftira tal-Ġobon

CHEESE FTIRA

INGREDIENTS

1 recipe dough
12 fresh sheep's cheese
4 eggs
sea salt and freshly cracked pepper
Flour for dusting
100ml extra virgin olive oil

METHOD

Open the dough on a floured surface to fit a baking tray

Cover the baking tray with the dough

In a bowl mix the cheese with the eggs and season

Spread the mixture on the dough and brush the edges with the oil

Bake in a hot oven at 240°C for about 10 minutes until nicely browned and crispy, serve immediately

Ftira bil-kline

FTIRA WITH ROSEMARY

INGREDIENTS

1 batch of Ftira dough
Fresh rosemary sprigs
Sea salt and fresh cracked pepper
400ml extra virgin olive oil
Flour for dusting

METHOD

Open the dough on a floured surface to fit a baking tray

Cover the baking tray with the dough and pierce with a fork

Brush with the oil; sprinkle some sea salt, pepper and the rosemary

Bake in a hot oven at 240°C for about 10 minutes until nicely browned and crispy and serve immediately

Brungiel il-forn
AUBERGINE CAVIAR

Few vegetables capture the colour, flavour and texture of the Mediterranean more than aubergine and here it is the star of the show, so much so that it is frequently now referred to as aubergine caviar. Mixed with any of the suggested additional ingredients, it really is a special treat.

Baked onions feature in the cuisine of many countries and the recipe on the page opposite features in the antipasti plates of many Gozitan celebrations.

INGREDIENTS

1 aubergine in its skin and gently washed
4 tablespoons extra virgin olive oil
1 teaspoon sea salt
5 basil leaves, shredded
3 garlic cloves, finely chopped

METHOD

Pierce the aubergine with a fork, several times and place on a baking sheet in a hot oven (200°C) and bake until soft to the touch (45 minutes to 1 hour)

Leave to rest for 15 minutes and scoop the flesh from the aubergine and then mix with the shredded basil leaves, garlic, sea salt and olive oil

Marinade for half an hour and eat accompanied by fresh crispy bread.

Tips: try adding any of the following additional ingredients

50g roasted pine nuts, a pinch of chilli flakes and some coriander

1 tsp lemon juice, 1 tablespoon chopped parsley, 1 small red onion finely shredded, together with peppered cheese shavings or 50g feta cheese.

For a tasty pasta dish shallow fry 100g smoked spiced sausage, toss with cooked pasta and then mix in the aubergine caviar recipe.

Basal il-forn
BAKED ONIONS

INGREDIENTS

6 large onions in their skin

4 tablespoons extra virgin olive oil

2 tablespoons shredded mint leaves

2 garlic cloves

Sea salt and freshly cracked black pepper

METHOD

Set the onions on an oven tray and bake at 200°C for 60 – 90 minutes until soft

Leave to rest for 20 minutes and then peel and cut them into large cubes

Mix in mint, garlic, extra virgin olive oil and seasoning to taste.

Tip: add roasted red pepper, sliced avocado and place on Romaine lettuce

Ġbejniet il-forn

BAKED SHEEP'S CHEESE WITH RED PEPPER SAUCE

This dish makes an elegant and subtle starter which goes well with toasted bread or salted crackers (try to find Galletti, another speciality of Malta and Gozo). If sheep's cheese is not available, you can substitute ricotta – it works just as well and when baked has a wonderful texture. Fresh herbs finely chopped form the coating for the cheese and provide the best flavour but dried herbs will also work (mixed thyme, parsley, basil etc.).

INGREDIENTS

For the red pepper sauce:
2 red peppers
1 ½ tbsp. of olive oil
1 small garlic clove crushed
1 small shallot, chopped roughly
85ml vegetable stock
½ tsp sugar (optional)

METHOD

Heat oven to 200° C/180° C fan/gas 6, and bake the herb-coated cheese for approx. 30 mins

Place the peppers on a baking tray and roast in the oven for about 45 minutes until the skins are blackened

Remove from the oven and put into a plastic bag - this makes them sweat and the skins slip off easily; when cool enough to handle, peel off the skins with your fingers.

Slice the peppers open, pick out and discard all the seeds and membrane, then roughly chop the red flesh.

Heat the olive oil in a frying pan; when hot, fry the garlic and shallot for a few minutes and then add the chopped peppers and continue to fry briefly, stirring to combine everything

Add the vegetable stock, bring to a gentle boil and allow it to reduce a little

Pour the contents of the pan into a blender and whizz until smooth, adjust seasoning to taste

Depending on the ripeness of the peppers, you shouldn't need any sugar - but if they retain a slightly bitter flavour, return the sauce to the pan, add sugar to taste and let it dissolve over the heat

Serve with the baked sheep's cheese.

Torta tat-tadam mixwi, ħabaq u basal

HILDA'S ROASTED TOMATO, BASIL AND ONION MARMALADE TART

Ripe tomatoes, oven baked to intensify the flavour; caramelised onion marmalade and fresh heady basil combine together to create a memorable tart ideal for family occasions. Best served with a mixed green salad, it is perfect for a summer lunch outside with a glass of Cold Gozitan Vermentino.

ONION MARMALADE

INGREDIENTS

1 tbsp. of olive oil
15g of butter
400g of onions finely chopped
1 tsp. fresh thyme

METHOD

Heat the olive oil and butter in a pan

Add onions, garlic and thyme, stir and cook over a medium heat for 45 mins

Stir occasionally until the onions are golden and caramelised

ROAST TOMATO TART

INGREDIENTS

1 packet of ready roll puff pastry
1 egg yolk beaten
4 anchovy fillets, chopped
8 pitted black olives
800g cherry tomatoes, halved
2 tsps. finely chopped thyme leaves
A little olive oil for drizzling
Sea salt and black pepper
Shredded basil leaves

METHOD

Preheat oven to 190° C

Unroll puff pastry and with a knife, make a 2-3 cm border mark around the edges

Brush with egg yolk

Spread the onion marmalade evenly over the pastry base and dot with the anchovies and olives

Arrange the halved tomatoes, cut side up on top and sprinkle with the thyme, salt and pepper

Bake for approx. 35 mins. until cooked and golden

Serve warm

Tip: try adding good quality sausage, either taken from its casing or sliced and gently fried in olive oil.

Pastizzi
GOZITAN HOME-MADE CHEESE CAKES

The Gozitan 'snack' par excellence', pastizzi (with either cheese or pea mixture) are hugely popular and on any Sunday in any square in Gozo, you will find locals (and tourists) happily tucking into these treats. The recipe below is for the more traditional baked cheese pastizzi. Be warned, they must be freshly made and are very addictive!

INGREDIENTS

For 4 cheese cakes, use half the torta pastry recipe (see page 33)

4 fresh sheep's cheese

200g broad beans removed from both outer and inner skins

50g golden raisins, washed and patted dry

1 egg

150ml extra virgin olive oil

Sea salt and freshly cracked pepper

METHOD

Cut the dough in 4 pieces and roll out on an oiled surface to form small disks

In a bowl mash the cheese with a fork, add the egg, beans, raisins and seasoning

Divide the mixture between the four disks and fold together, crimp the edges and bake in moderate hot oven at 200°C for approximately 30 minutes.

Kunserva
SUN DRIED TOMATO PASTE

If there is one item that best captures the taste of Gozo, it has to be the humble tomato – probably Gozo's most important produce; over 10,000 tons of tomatoes are produced annually with much of it turned into the hugely popular Kunserva or sun dried tomato paste. Nowadays, much of the Kunserva is produced in factories but on estates such as Ta'Mena, Kunserva is still produced in the traditional manner (as it is in many Gozitan homes) relying directly on the July/August daytime Mediterranean sun to dry the paste and to concentrate the flavour and quality of this, now officially recognised, Gozitan product. Kunserva is used in every home across the island in many different dishes adding a stunning depth, flavour and colour but, it is, perhaps at its most popular in Hobż biż-żejt – the quintessential Gozitan 'sandwich'. Once you have tried one, there is no going back!

HOBŻ BIŻ-ŻEJT

The name Hobż biż-żejt literally translates as 'bread with oil'. Thick slices of local bread are spread with sweetish tomato paste and topped with capers, olives, garlic, black pepper and a drizzle of olive oil; sometimes tuna or anchovies are added.

INGREDIENTS

A hobża or loaf of the best crusty bread available

Good quality Kunserva/tomato paste

Capers

White anchovies or tinned tuna in oil, drained

Sea salt and pepper

Flat leaf parsley, leaves picked

Extra virgin olive oil (peppered sheep's cheese can also be added)

METHOD

Pour the olive oil on a plate

Spread tomato paste over slices of bread

Place the bread, kunserva side down on to the plate to soak in the oil

Add the capers

Top with anchovies or tuna

Season with sea salt and freshly ground pepper

Add the parsley and drizzle with some extra virgin olive oil.

Baker David Mercieca

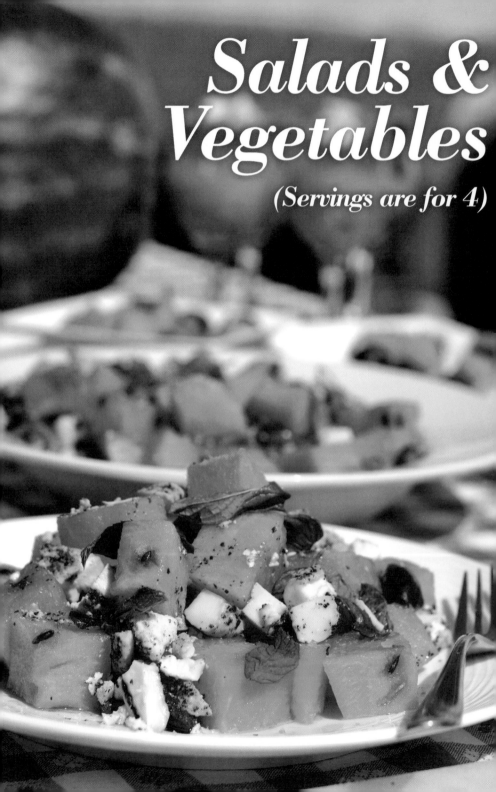

Salads & Vegetables

(Servings are for 4)

Insalata tad-dulliegħ

WATERMELON, PEPPERED CHEESE & MINT

Ripe, red and juicy watermelon; peppery cheese and fresh mint with olive oil dressing – a mix to capture summer and to please family and friends. If you haven't already tried it, do – you will not be disappointed. If Gozo's peppered ġbejniet are not available, try good quality feta, add freshly ground pepper and make sure the watermelon is ripe.

The second salad here is one of the easiest to make – don't skimp on the garlic – this is a robust, full-flavoured salad.

The following pages offer a range of additional fresh and mouth-watering salads featuring a variety of different Gozitan ingredients plus some suggested salad dressings.

INGREDIENTS

1 kg ripe sweet water melon, white rind removed, deseeded and cut into chunks

4 peppered sheep's cheese, broken loosely into medium sized pieces

16 black olives, stoned and halved

1 small bunch of fresh mint leaves

1 tsp. sea salt

30cl extra virgin olive oil

METHOD

Gently mix the melon, cheese and olives

Divide among the plates, top up with the mint and dress with olive oil and sea salt.

Fażola bit-tewm u tursin

BUTTER BEAN, PARSLEY & GARLIC

INGREDIENTS

400g butter beans

4 fresh garlic or garlic cloves, chopped

4 tablespoons extra virgin olive oil

Bunch parsley, finely chopped

Sea salt and freshly cracked black pepper

METHOD

If using dried butter beans, soak them overnight and then place in a saucepan with enough water to cover and bring to the boil, simmer gently until cooked; add extra hot water if necessary to prevent the beans from drying, then strain and let cool

If using canned beans (these are just as good), rinse and drain them well

Mix the beans with the olive oil, garlic, parsley, salt and pepper and serve cold accompanied by crusty bread with tomato paste

Insalata tal-ġbejniet u tadam

FRESH SHEEP'S CHEESE & TOMATO

INGREDIENTS

4 fresh sheep's cheese, sliced; 8 plump tomatoes, washed and sliced thickly; 1 small bunch fresh oregano, chopped (dried oregano will work well also); 1 small bunch rocket; 50ml extra virgin olive oil; sea salt and freshly cracked pepper.

METHOD

Place rocket on the base of the salad plate or bowl, top with the tomatoes and the cheese, sprinkle the oregano, pepper and salt and finish with a drizzle of oil.

Insalata tal- ġbejniet u qarabagħli

COURGETTE, CHILLI, LEMON & SHEEP'S CHEESE

INGREDIENTS

4 courgettes, finely sliced; 4 fresh sheep's cheese, sliced; 1 small red chilli, finely chopped; zest of 1 lemon; 1 small bunch fresh mint leaves; 50cl extra virgin olive oil; sea salt and freshly cracked pepper.

METHOD

Heat a griddle pan or barbeque and grill the courgettes on each side until lightly charred. Place the warm courgettes on a tray and season with salt, pepper, chilli and olive oil and leave to marinate for 15 minutes. Arrange the courgettes on the salad plate or bowl, reserving the oils and juices. Top with the fresh cheese and the mint leaves and sprinkle with lemon zest and drizzle with the courgette marinade.

Insalata tat-tonn taż-żejt

TUNA, RED ONION, CANNELLINI BEAN & BASIL

INGREDIENTS

2 garlic cloves, crushed; 1 tablespoon sherry vinegar; 75ml extra virgin olive oil; 400g cannellini beans rinsed and drained; 1 large red onion, finely chopped; 400g of good quality tuna in oil 2 handfuls of basil, shredded; sea salt and freshly cracked pepper.

METHOD

In a bowl mix the oil, vinegar, garlic and a pinch of salt. Mix the dressing with the beans and onions gently, add the tuna and finish off with the basil and some fresh pepper. Serves 4.

Insalata tal-laring

OMAR'S ORANGE, RED ONION, CHILLI & ROCKET

We were introduced to this brilliant and hugely popular salad by our good friend Omar Grech.

INGREDIENTS

2 sweet oranges, peeled, pith removed and carefully sliced, retaining the juice; 1 small red onion, thinly sliced; 1 large chilli, thinly sliced ; a bunch of rocket leaves

METHOD

Assemble the ingredients gently on a bed of the rocket leaves and drizzle over with the reserved orange juice and olive oil.

Insalata tal-fenek

WARM RABBIT

INGREDIENTS

Half a deboned rabbit, cut into small cubes

100g white grapes, skin and seeds removed

Small bunches of celery, mint, rocket and parsley leaves

2 tablespoons Gozo bees' honey

10ml sweet white vermouth

2 tablespoons raspberry vinegar

200ml extra virgin olive oil

Sea salt and freshly cracked pepper

1 tablespoon whole grain mustard

METHOD

Marinate the rabbit with the vinegar and freshly cracked pepper, leave to rest for 2 hours

Mix the honey, mustard and half the oil together

Heat 50ml oil in a pan and sweat the grapes for 2 minutes, stir in the vermouth, season and reduce the sauce by half

Heat the remaining oil and sauté the rabbit with the marinade for about 10 minutes

Dress the salad leaves with the dressing, spoon on the warm rabbit and top up with the grapes, and finish with freshly cracked pepper.

Insalata taz-zalzett Għawdxi u arzell

CREAMY BEAN, SCALLOPS & SMOKED GOZITAN SAUSAGE

INGREDIENTS

300g scallops

150g smoked sausage, sliced

200g butter beans, rinsed and drained

1 garlic clove, finely chopped

Juice of 1 lemon

small bunch rocket leaves

2 handfuls of parsley and celery leaves

handful celery leaves

100ml extra virgin olive oil

15ml cider vinegar

Sea salt and freshly cracked pepper

METHOD

Mash the beans with the garlic and some olive oil and season well

Mix the leaves with the oil, vinegar and seasoning

Heat a pan and add the sausage without adding oil and grill until crisp on each side, remove and add the scallops, cook on each side for 1 minute, pour in the lemon juice and let it bubble

Place the marinated on a salad plate in the form of a ring, spoon the bean pate in the middle, top up with the scallops and finish with the sausage

Sprinkle some sea salt and pepper and serve.

Kondiment ta' l-insalata

EIGHT SALAD DRESSINGS

Bil-lumi | LEMON
Mix 1 lemon juice with 120ml extra virgin olive oil.

Bl-għasel | HONEY
Mix 120ml extra virgin olive oil, 2 tablespoons whole grain mustard, 2 tablespoons bees honey, 10ml raspberry vinegar.

Bit-tursin | PARSLEY
Finely chop small bunch of parsley, 1 spring onion, 100ml extra virgin olive oil, 30ml red wine vinegar, sea salt and freshly cracked pepper.

Bl-inċova | ANCHOVY
Finely chop 1 anchovy fillet, 1 tablespoon capers, small bunch parsley and 1 garlic clove, mix together with 100ml extra virgin olive oil and 20ml red wine vinegar.

Bil-filfel | CHILLI
Finely chop 1 medium sized chilli removing the seeds, mix with 120 ml extra virgin olive oil, 20 ml red wine vinegar, sea salt and freshly cracked pepper.

Bit-tadam | TOMATO
Skin and deseed 2 tomatoes and liquidise to a runny liquid, mix with 120 ml extra virgin olive oil, 30g balsamic mustard, 1 spring onion, sea salt and freshly cracked pepper

Biż-żebbuġ | OLIVE
Crushed 12 black olives mixed with 1 tablespoon oregano and 120ml extra virgin olive oil.

Bil-frawli | STRAWBERRY
Whiz 5 fresh strawberries; mix with 30ml balsamic vinegar and 120ml extra virgin olive oil, freshly cracked pepper.

Torta tal-ġbejniet u ful
CHEESE, POTATO & BROAD BEAN PIE

Pies of various types are hugely popular in Gozo reflecting the influence of British food culture; the pie here is one of the most popular, especially when the beans are at their best in the late spring. The pie is delicious served warm and even at room temperature and goes extremely well with a good home-made chutney or a sweet chilli sauce.

INGREDIENTS

For a 15cm pie dish half the torta recipe (see below)

1 potato, peeled and finely sliced

4 fresh sheep's cheese

200g skinned broad beans

sea salt and white pepper

150ml extra virgin olive oil

METHOD

Roll out the pastry on an oiled surface; line a 15cm pie dish leaving pastry flaps hanging over the edges

In a bowl mash the cheese, add the beans and seasoning

Lay the potatoes at the bottom of the pie dish and top up with the cheese mixture

Fold the flaps back and cook in a moderate oven at 180°C for approximately 35 minutes (pastry should be golden crunchy)

Leave to rest for 10 minutes and serve.

Note: the base of the pie will remain soft – this is part of the fun of the dish.

Għaġina tat-torta
TORTA BASIC PASTRY RECIPE

INGREDIENTS

1kg white flour

Water as needed

300g salted butter (at room temperature)

½ tsp. salt

METHOD

Put the flour in a mixing bowl with the salt; add enough water to make a stiff dough

Work on medium speed for some time. Leave the dough to rest for ½ an hour

Roll pastry on a floured top and spread butter evenly over the whole surface, using your hands.

Roll up as for a Swiss roll and leave to rest, preferably in a refrigerator for at least 1 hour. Now it is ready to be used. Cut small pieces as required and open them either on floured surface or on oiled surface.

Torta tal-qargħa aħmar

PUMPKIN AND RICE PIE

INGREDIENTS

For a 15cm pie dish half the torta pastry recipe (see previous page)

500g pumpkin cut into small cubes

150g par boiled rice, drained and rinsed under cold water

1 onion, finely chopped

small bunch basil leaves shredded

15 pitted green olives

100g tuna in oil (optional)

Sea salt and freshly cracked pepper

60ml extra virgin olive oil

2 eggs

50g parmesan cheese grated

METHOD

Line a 15cm pie dish with the pastry leaving pastry flaps hanging over the edges

Add the oil to a heated pan and sauté the onion until golden, add the pumpkin and shallow fry until tender, mix in the olives and basil and cook for a further 2 minutes (at this stage add the tuna if using)

Stir the mixture into the rice, mix in the eggs and the grated cheese

Fill the pie dish and fold back the flaps and cook in a moderate oven at 180°C for approximately 35 minutes (pastry should be golden and crunchy)

Leave to rest for 10 minutes and serve

Tadam mimli bil-brunġiel

STUFFED TOMATOES WITH AUBERGINES

INGREDIENTS

8 large tomatoes, tops cut off and deseeded

1 small aubergine, cut into small cubes

12 basil leaves shredded

1 slice crusty bread

200ml extra virgin olive oil

1 tsp capers, finely chopped

8 black olives, finely chopped

small bunch parsley, finely chopped

Sea salt and freshly cracked pepper

METHOD

Dredge the aubergine cubes with salt, leave for half an hour, rinse under cold water and pat dry

Heat a pan with the oil and sauté the aubergines until golden, add the olives and herbs and cook for a further 2 minutes

Stir in the bread and the capers and remove from heat

Fill the tomatoes with the aubergine mixture and put on an oven tray

Bake at 200°C for a few minutes, leaving the tomato still firm.

Tadam mimli bil-faqqiegħ u qaqoċċ

STUFFED TOMATOES WITH MUSHROOMS & ARTICHOKE HEARTS

INGREDIENTS

8 large tomatoes

200g button mushrooms

400g Portobello mushrooms

4 globe artichokes, outer leaves removed and hearts cut into small cubes

100g walnuts shelled and roughly chopped

4 garlic cloves, finely chopped

Small bunch parsley, finely chopped

½ tsp chilli flakes

12 basil leaves, chopped

200ml extra virgin olive oil

Sea salt and freshly cracked pepper

METHOD

Heat the pan with half the oil and put in the artichokes, cook until golden and crisp

Stir in half the garlic and the button mushrooms, cook for a further 5 minutes and then season and add half the parsley

In another pan heat the remaining oil and sauté the portobello mushrooms until golden, stir in the garlic, chilli and walnuts and cook for a further 3 minutes; then remove from heat and add the parsley and basil, season to taste

Fill the tomatoes with the first mixture and bake in a hot oven at 200°C for a few minutes, leaving the tomatoes still firm

Serve the tomatoes on top of the portobello mixture.

GOZO'S HIDDEN TREASURE

Wine production in the Maltese Islands precedes the Roman domination of the Mediterranean and can be traced to the Phoenician/Punic period dating back to around 1000 BC as has been highlighted by recent excavations at Mgarr ix-Xini in Gozo.

The climatic conditions of the archipelago are very well suited for the growing of grapes for high quality wines; this is especially so in Gozo which is a smaller island and is more exposed to cool north-westerly and westerly winds thus having a more temperate climate than Malta. This is an advantage especially for red wines.

The soil in Gozo has a loamy character and is generally richer than in Malta with the effect that productivity of the same vine per hectare is potentially higher. In addition, the more passionate wine makers in Gozo practice green pruning (the removal of immature grape bunches) to enhance quality and the environment is a little more saline than in Malta (Gozo being smaller) which is an added bonus as far as flavour enhancement is concerned.

As a result, Gozo is in an excellent position to produce wines of the highest quality depending only on the degree of passion of the wine maker concerned. In general a good Gozo wine should show character, robustness as well as balance. Indeed it is the latter characteristic which can make Gozo wines unique. Perfect harvest timing is essential in this regard.

Although Gozo has an edge in the production of reds, the whites can also be of the highest quality. For example, the Chardonnay and Vermentino wines at Ta'Mena estate show all these Gozo characteristics well. The balance between alcohol, acid and polyphenols is very pleasant on the palate with an expression of fruitiness characteristic of the grape that is pineapple on chardonnay and apricot on Vermentino. The barrel-fermented Chardonnay certainly merits the label of a great wine. Its peach/honey flavour combines very well with soft, delicate cheeses to render unforgettable sensations.

Reds are, as expected, round in taste, robust with enough acid to show great character. A wine worth searching out is the very popular 1551 (now produced by Gawdex Wines). The roundness in taste in particular is due to the ripe soft tannins which come about only in perfect climatic conditions and perfect harvest timing. In effect the ageing time required for these wines in oak barriques can be of a limited nature, certainly months and not years.

The soil element in all Gozo wines manifests itself (especially in whites) as a very slight bitterness in the aftertaste, which contributes to character and specificity. This characteristic renders the white wines particularly thirst-

quenching at the right serving temperature. Too many locals and visitors still believe that local Gozo wines do not stand up to better known international wines but a sampling of Gozo's best will very quickly dispel this myth!

Carmel Rapa is one of Gozo's well-known wine makers

GOZO WINE TODAY

Since the late 1970's and early 80's, there has been what could be termed a 'revolution' in wine making in both Malta and Gozo resulting in a significant shift in the style, characteristics and quality of local wines. This is mainly due to the viticulture revival that happened as some of the island's larger wineries began planting new and larger vineyards growing international varieties. This development has been important to local wine-making, because it has facilitated the production of much higher quality wines, while also allowing significant diversification in the types of wines produced. Earlier experiments had showed that in spite of the mild winters and the hot summers, established international grape varieties could be grown in Malta with excellent results. The fact that many local wines have now been recognised internationally and have won accolades illustrates the point.

Today the main grape varieties grown on the Maltese islands include the two indigenous varieties Gellewza (red) and Ghirgentina (white), as well as international varieties including Cabernet Sauvignon, Merlot, Syrah (or Shiraz), Cabernet Franc, Chardonnay, Sauvignon Blanc, Moscato and more.

The reputation of Maltese wines has traditionally been poor with inferior wine being the norm and this has left a legacy of scepticism and resistance to local wines. However, this is all now changing utterly as in May 2007 Malta introduced its own D.O.K. ('protected denomination of origin') and I.G.T.

('protected geographical indication') production protocols. These wine categories (with separate protocols for D.O.K. wines from Malta and from Gozo) were introduced with the aim of increasing the overall quality, improving control of the various aspects of wine production and providing consumers with a guaranteed degree of quality. By April 2012, there were sixteen registered commercial wine producers; five of these in Gozo; ten wineries are registered for the production of 'Quality Wines' (those with a D.O.K. or I.G.T). The control protocols are the responsibility of the Ministry for Agriculture, which determines which wines qualify under which classification.

Estate Wines are a particular category of Quality Wines that are produced from wine grapes of a very high quality. What distinguishes these wines from other quality wines is that they can only be produced from wine grapes that are cultivated in the vineyards that are managed by the winery itself.

In 2010, the total production of wine (i.e. Quality Wine and Table Wine) from grapes cultivated in Malta and Gozo amounted to over 1.8 million bottles, 91% of which were 'Quality Wines'. Typical of the latter Gozitan wines are those now produced by newcomers Gaudex Wines with their very popular 1551, tal Latini, Enchor and Gabillot ranges. The titles and labels betray a considerable amount about the history, culture and topography of Gozitan wine.

GABILLOTT®

red

GOZO
D.O.K.
Marsalforn Valley
Vintage 2009

GAUDEX
WINES
Isle of Gozo, Malta

75cl℮   13% vol.

1551®

Land ✳ Roots ✳ Vines

GOZO
D.O.K.
SERKUZAN-SYRAH
2009

from the
Marsalforn Valley

GAUDEX
WINES
Isle of Gozo, Malta

75cl℮   13% vol.

*Joseph Fiteni at Ta' Mena
Winery during the harvest*

41

Pasta & Risotto
(Servings are for 4)

Risotto tat-tadam u ġbejniet

ROASTED TOMATO AND SHEEP'S CHEESE RISOTTO

Despite its reputation, risotto is very quick and easy to make – the secret is to always use the best stock available; if you are under time pressure, there are now many high quality stocks available but, as ever, a home-made stock is easy to do and maximises the depth of flavour.

INGREDIENTS

Vegetable stock (app 1.5ltr)
2 potatoes; 2 onions; 2 leeks; 2 carrots; 1 kohlrabi (or similar root vegetable); 2 celery sticks; 4 parsley stalks; pinch of sea salt

Roasted tomatoes
800g fresh tomatoes, cut into cubes
2 garlic cloves, finely chopped
1 tsp. marjoram, finely chopped
1 tsp. thyme finely chopped
50ml extra virgin olive oil
sea salt and freshly ground pepper

Risotto
Finely chopped one onion
65g butter
350g Arborio rice
1.5ltr vegetable stock
Roasted tomatoes
40ml extra virgin olive oil
2 fresh sheep cheese cut into small pieces (they can be exchanged with 50g fresh mozzarella or 50g goat cheese for a more robust flavour)

Chilli dressing (optional)
25ml chilli oil
5 capers finely chopped
5 fresh mint leaves
1 garlic clove
100g rocket

METHOD

First make the vegetable stock by peeling, washing and roughly cutting all the vegetables; place them in a large sauce pan, add 1.7ltr water, a pinch of sea salt and bring to the boil; reduce heat and simmer for at least 20 min, drain retaining both the stock and the cooked vegetables (see note below)

Mix the other ingredients together with the oil and transfer to a roasting tray; drizzle with freshly ground black pepper and sea salt and roast in a moderate hot oven at 180°C for approximately 1hr or until slightly charred but not burnt

For the dressing put chilli oil, capers, mint leaves and garlic in a food processor and blitz together

Melt the butter in a saucepan, add the onion and cook over a low heat, stirring occasionally for 8min; stir in the rice and cook, stirring, until the grains are coated, then add the roasted tomatoes with all the juices

Add a ladleful of the hot stock and cook, stirring, until it has been absorbed

Continue adding the stock, a ladleful at a time, and stirring until it has been absorbed, season to taste; this will take about 20 minutes

When the rice is tender, stir in the oil and the fresh cheese and allow to rest for 2 minutes

Serve accompanied by fresh rocket leaves dressed with chilli dressing.

Note: the vegetables from the stock can make an appetising dish in themselves served cold or warm drizzled with extra virgin olive oil, sea salt and freshly cracked pepper and crispy bread.

Ravjul tal-Ġbejniet
FRESH SHEEP'S CHEESE RAVIOLI

Ravioli is universally popular and any good Gozitan restaurant serves it as a matter of local pride; the favourite being stuffed with fresh sheep's cheese and then served with the tomato sauce described on page 44. The photo set on the opposite page will help you make fresh ravioli if you haven't tried to do so before. Do give it a go, apart from the fun, it is very satisfactory to make from scratch.

INGREDIENTS

For the dough:
150g plain flour
100g semolina
pinch of salt
water (as needed)
1 tsp. olive oil

For the filling:
4 fresh sheep cheese
1 tbsp. grated parmesan cheese
1 small bunch parsley, finely chopped
sea salt and freshly cracked pepper
1 egg

For serving:
1 recipe traditional tomato sauce (see page 46) and 100g grated parmesan cheese.

METHOD

Mix the dough ingredients together and then briefly knead with water as necessary until you have semi-hard but elastic dough

Mix all the filling ingredients in a bowl

Roll out the dough on a floured surface to a 2 mm thickness; then cut 8cm disks, brush with a little water, put 1 tsp. of the filling in the middle of each disk, fold in two and press round the edges

Cook in boiling salted water for approximately 6 minutes, depending on the thickness of the dough

Drain and serve with the tomato sauce and grated cheese.

Note: leftover cooked ravioli are nicely served deep fried the day after; also serve them with the tomato sauce.

Zlazi tat-Tadam
FOUR TOMATO SAUCES

Tar-Ravjul

TRADITIONAL RAVIOLI TOMATO SAUCE

INGREDIENTS

3 garlic cloves, finely chopped
50g sweet sun-dried tomato paste
20ml extra virgin olive oil
sea salt and freshly cracked pepper
300ml water

METHOD

Heat the oil in a small pan, add the garlic and cook slightly for about 20seconds, mix in the tomato paste and dilute with water

Season with salt and pepper; reduce the sauce on slow heat to a thick consistency

This sauce is traditionally served with ravioli but it can be served with any pasta dish.

Ta' l-Għaġin

TOMATO SAUCE NORMALLY SERVED WITH PASTA

INGREDIENTS

400g small sweet tomatoes, roughly chopped

2 garlic cloves, peeled and lightly pressed

75ml extra virgin olive oil

small bunch of fresh basil leaves, shredded

Sea salt and freshly cracked pepper

METHOD

Heat the pan with the oil, add the garlic and fry very briefly

Mix in the tomatoes, season and cook for a further 7 minutes

Remove the garlic, add the basil and serve.

Bit-tadam frisk

RAW TOMATO SAUCE

INGREDIENTS

600g fresh plum tomatoes, deseeded and cut into small cubes

2 garlic cloves, finely chopped

Small bunch of basil leaves, shredded

sea salt and freshly cracked pepper

150ml cold press olive oil

METHOD

In a bowl mix tomatoes, garlic, basil and oil, cover with cling film and marinate for 1 hour

Just before serving adjust seasoning.

Bit-tadam ahdar

GREEN TOMATO SAUCE

INGREDIENTS

300g green tomatoes, deseeded and finely chopped

1 white onion, finely chopped

1 small chilli, crushed

1 garlic cloves, finely chopped

2 bay leaves

50ml extra virgin olive oil

1 tsp. sugar

sea salt and freshly cracked pepper

METHOD

Heat a pan with the oil, add the onion and the garlic and cook covered for approximately 5 minutes

When onion is tender, mix in the tomatoes, chilli, bay leaves and sugar and simmer for few minutes

Season with the salt and fresh pepper.

Tagliatelle bil-klamari u qaqoċċ

DANIEL'S TAGLIATELLE WITH BABY CALAMARI & ARTICHOKES

Daniel Magrin is well known and respected in Xaghra for the quality and style of his food. This is one of his typical pasta dishes, easily re-created at home and packed with flavour.

On the following pages, I also include additional, easy to prepare pasta dishes using easily accessible ingredients.

INGREDIENTS

400g of tagliatelle

4 tbsp. extra virgin olive oil

4 cloves of garlic

3 tbsp. basil chopped

500g quartered artichoke hearts

600g baby calamari

METHOD

Bring a large pot of salted water to the boil, add the Tagliatelle and cook until al dente

Meanwhile, in a large pan over high heat, warm the olive oil and add the garlic, cook until golden in colour

Add the baby calamari and cook for 2 minutes, then add the quartered artichokes and cook for 6-7 minutes

Drain the pasta and toss in the pan

Add the chopped basil, salt and pepper to taste and serve immediately.

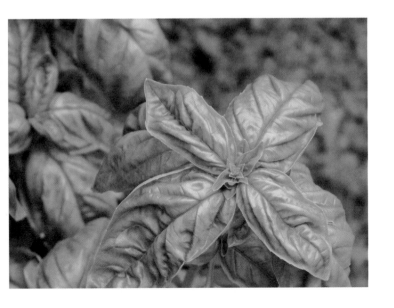

Spaghetti bil-lumi, ħabaq u tursin
SPAGHETTI WITH LEMON, BASIL & PARSLEY

INGREDIENTS

400g pasta spaghetti

The zest and juice of 2 unwaxed lemons

Small bunch parsley, finely chopped

small bunch basil, shredded

Sea salt and freshly cracked pepper

100ml extra virgin olive oil

METHOD

Put the zest in a small pan of boiling water, simmer for 5 minutes and pat dry

In a bowl mix the parsley, basil, zest, juice and olive oil

Boil the pasta in plenty of boiling salted water until al dente, drain the pasta and toss in the lemon and herb mixture, season to taste and serve immediately.

Note: this dish can also be made with parmesan or pecorino cheese added.

Pappardelle biz-zalza tal-fenek
PAPPARDELLE WITH RABBIT SAUCE

INGREDIENTS

400g Pappardelle

half deboned rabbit

1 fennel bulb, peeled and sliced

20 cherry tomatoes, halved

3 bay leaves

3 sprigs thyme

1 sprig rosemary

4 garlic cloves, finely chopped

30cl sweet white wine

small bunch parsley, finely chopped

Sea salt and freshly cracked pepper

150ml extra virgin olive oil

METHOD

Cut the rabbit in small cubes and marinade with the chopped thyme, rosemary, pepper and wine overnight in the fridge

Remove the rabbit from the marinade and reserve

Heat half the oil in a pan, put the garlic and the rabbit and cook until it is browned all over, stir in the marinade and the bay leaves and simmer for about 35 minutes, if the liquid evaporates, add a little water to obtain a juicy sauce

In a separate pan heat the remaining oil and sauté the fennel until golden and crisp, add the cherry tomatoes, season and remove from heat

Put the pasta in boiling salted water and cook for 6 minutes or until al dente, drain and mix in the rabbit sauce and the fennel mixture

Finish with the parsley and a dash of oil.

Spaghetti bit-tadam frisk
SPAGHETTI WITH MEDITERRANEAN TOMATO SAUCE

INGREDIENTS

350g spaghetti

600g ripe tomatoes, skin removed, deseeded and finely chopped

20 pitted black olives

4 tablespoons capers, rinsed

2 anchovy fillets, chopped

small bunch basil leaves, shredded

Freshly cracked pepper

2 sun-dried tomatoes in oil, finely shredded

150ml extra virgin olive oil

4 garlic cloves

METHOD

Mix together the tomatoes, oil, olives, capers, sun-dried tomatoes, anchovy, basil, freshly cracked pepper and leave to rest in a warm place for 2 hours (or gently heat over the pasta as it cooks)

Cook the pasta in boiling salted water, until al dente, drain and put it in the bowl of the tomato mixture

Stir and serve immediately.

Għaġin bil-Gambli

PASTA WITH PRAWNS, CHILLI, LEMON & ROCKET

INGREDIENTS

400g dried spaghetti

7 tablespoons extra virgin olive oil

4 cloves of garlic, crushed

2 medium hot chillies, chopped

150g cherry tomatoes, quartered

Zest and juice of 1 lemon

500g fresh medium prawns

4 basil leaves

1 sprig marjoram

50ml Vermentino wine

Sea salt and freshly cracked pepper

Good handful of rocket leaves

METHOD

Heat 1 tablespoon oil, add 1 garlic clove skin on and fry briefly

Add the basil leaves, the marjoram, the prawns and sauté for a couple of minutes

Then deglaze the pan with wine, season and cook for further 2 minutes

Remove the prawns, strain and reserve the juice

Put the pasta in boiling salted water for about 6 minutes

In the meantime heat a pan with the remaining oil, add the garlic and the chilli, cook for a few seconds (be careful not to burn the garlic)

Add the cherry tomatoes and cook for 2 minutes, stir in the lemon juice and half the zest

Finally, add the prawns and the pasta, top up with the cooked prawn juice, season and cook for a further 2 minutes, until all juice is absorbed

Finish with the shredded rocket and serve.

Serves 4.

My colleague, Andrew Busuttil

Għaġin bil-Gambli, asperagu u piżelli friska
CLAIRE'S PASTA WITH PRAWNS, ASPARAGUS & PEAS

INGREDIENTS

500g ditali pasta

1 bunch trimmed asparagus (about 400g)

3 tbsp chopped fresh garlic

200g shelled fresh peas

1 tsp finely sliced lemon zest

60ml white wine

1 shot brandy

24 local fresh prawns

Some extra virgin olive oil

Salt and pepper

some finely chopped fresh parsley

1 tsp fresh marjoram

METHOD

Trim the tips of the asparagus and set aside. Finely slice the stems and keep side.

Bring a large pot of salted water to the boil.

add the pasta and the peas and cook according to the pack instructions.

Whilst the pasta is cooking, gently warm the oil and garlic being careful not to burn the garlic. Add the chopped asparagus and wine and cook for 2 minutes. Add the prawns, lemon zest, marjoram and brandy and cook for about 5 to 8 minutes. Add the asparagus tips, heat through and switch off.

Drain the pasta and peas and add to the asparagus and prawns. Toss until everything mixed evenly. Drizzle with olive oil, season with salt and pepper (even chili if desired) and sprinkle with chopped parsley. Mix, leave to rest for 5 minutes and serve. Can be eaten cold.

Serves 4.

Bebbux mimli
PASTA SHELLS WITH FRESH CHEESE

INGREDIENTS

1 serving of raw tomato sauce (page 47)

320g large pasta shells

350g fresh sheep's cheese

50g grated cheese (parmesan or pecorino)

small bunch parsley, finely chopped

1 litre milk

Sea salt and freshly cracked pepper

100ml extra virgin olive oil

METHOD

In a bowl mix the cheese with the parsley and season to taste

Spread the raw tomato sauce evenly in an oven dish

Fill the pasta shells with the cheese and place them snuggly together on the tomato sauce, the cheese facing up

Pour in the milk until it almost covers the shells completely

Season with salt and pepper and bake in a moderate oven 180°C for about 25 minutes or until almost all the liquid is absorbed

Serve immediately with a drizzle of extra virgin olive oil.

Zalza tad-tadam
TOMATO KETCHUP

INGREDIENTS

2kg ripe tomatoes skin and seeds removed

1 red onion and 3 garlic cloves, finely chopped

1 teaspoon fresh mild chilli

100g dark brown sugar

100ml red wine vinegar

1 teaspoon grain mustard, ½ teaspoon paprika, ½ teaspoon mixed spice, ½ teaspoon ground cinnamon

10g fresh ginger peeled

Sea salt and freshly cracked pepper

METHOD

Place the tomatoes, onions, garlic, chilli, sugar, vinegar, salt and pepper in a blender and mix to a fine puree. Add in all the other ingredients and blend again. Pass the mixture through a fine sieve, put in a deep pan and simmer for 4 hours or until the sauce is thick. Cool, put in glass jars and refrigerate.

Spaghetti biz-zalzett u faqqiegħ

SPAGHETTI WITH LOCAL SAUSAGE & MUSHROOMS

The quality of Gozo's produce is highlighted brilliantly in its very high quality pork from producers such as Mark from Dwardu's butchers in Sannat. He produces a very broad range of great products and supplies many of the island's best restaurants and hotels. Here his sausages (also available smoked) are combined with mushrooms, local chardonnay and herbs to produce a simple yet full flavoured pasta that you'll add to your 'will do again' list.

INGREDIENTS

400g spaghetti

2 garlic cloves, finely chopped

150g local pork sausage, taken out of the casing and chopped finely

10 basil leaves, shredded

100g cultivated white mushrooms, ends trimmed and cut into quarters

1 small bunch of parsley, finely chopped

75ml chardonnay wine

50ml extra virgin olive oil

Sea salt and freshly cracked pepper

METHOD

In a large pan, heat half the oil over high heat, add the mushrooms and cook until golden, about 5 minutes

Add the garlic, reduce the heat, add the wine and cook until it has evaporated

Put in the sausage meat and cook for about 3 minutes, stir in the basil and the parsley and leave to the side

Put the pasta in salted boiling water and cook for about 6 minutes; drain reserving some liquid

Mix the pasta with the sauce, add some of the pasta liquid and cook for further 2 minutes

Season to taste and serve immediately with a drizzle of oil.

Mark Agius of Dwardu's butchers in Sannat

Ilma Żahar

ORANGE FLOWER WATER

Ilma Żahar is a clear, perfumed distillation of fresh bitter orange blossoms and is made every year in May/June by Maria Assunta Bajada and her son Lawrence in Xaghra (the distilling equipment is kept in the local police station for the remainder of the year!). It is made by macerating bitter orange blossom in water and then distilling the broth. Orange blossoms are traditionally seen as the romantic bridal flower.

Ilma Żahar is a very traditional product with many uses from cooking to health (it is recommended for stomach upsets and pains, for example); it is also widely used in the cooking of North Africa, the Middle East and in Mediterranean countries such as Malta. It is a beautiful but strong and robust ingredient and so a little is the order of the day. While it is often difficult to obtain pure orange flower water (supermarkets often have more processed versions), this isn't so in Gozo where local housewives and cooks purchase the real thing from the Bajadas.

Ilma Żahar is used today in traditional Maltese desserts, such as mqaret (see page 90), kwareżimal (honey cakes; the name itself is a reference to the *quaresima* or 40 days of Lent) and figolli (traditional Easter biscuits made with almond paste covered in coloured icing and usually made in a festive shape as a rabbit or a fish).

An excellent (Moroccan inspired) salad can be made using grated carrot, dressed with olive oil and lemon juice, then sprinkled with orange flower water and finished off with pine nuts.

L-imqarrun il-forn tal-ma

MUM'S BAKED MACARONI

INGREDIENTS

400g dried macaroni

1 large onion, roughly chopped

300g mixed minced beef and pork

4 thin steaks of pork neck

100g sliced smoked bacon, rind removed and diced

50g tomato paste

2 fresh sheep's cheese or 100g ricotta

100g grated parmesan cheese

2 eggs

30ml extra virgin olive oil

Sea salt and freshly cracked pepper

METHOD

Heat a deep pan with the oil and fry the pork neck for 2 minutes on each side, season and set aside

In the same pan cook the onions until golden, add the mince and cook for a further 10 minutes, stirring occasionally

Add the bacon and stir in the tomato paste, simmer for about 10 more minutes and allow to cool

Bring a large pan of salted water to the boil and add the pasta, cook for 5minutes, leaving the pasta firm to the touch; drain, cool and season the pasta

Add half the parmesan cheese, the fresh cheese, the sauce and finally the beaten eggs to the pasta

Pour half the mixture in a non-stick oven pan; add the sautéed pork neck and top up with the remaining pasta mixture

Finish with the remaining grated cheese and bake in a moderate oven at 180°C for 30 minutes until pasta is golden

Leave to rest and then serve.

Note: any left over pasta can be easily re-heated the next day and served with a tomato sauce or eaten cold at room temperature.

Fish
(Servings are for 4)

Denċi l-forn
ROAST DENĊI WITH A NICOISE SAUCE

Inevitably fish is hugely popular in Gozo and the variety is considerable. In this recipe, Denċi (Dentex) is combined with four different herbs to produce a wonderfully aromatic, tasty and yet, robust dish. If you can get them, the wild fennel fronds (they grow everywhere in Gozo) add an extra special touch. Serve this dish with rice.

INGREDIENTS

1 kg of fish

Sea salt and black pepper

Olive oil for brushing

For the sauce

200 g tinned tomatoes or 6 fresh tomatoes, skinned and deseeded

2 garlic cloves, crushed

2 tablespoons olive oil

125 ml white wine

250 ml fish stock

Leaves from 2 sprigs of thyme

Leaves from 2-3 sprigs of tarragon, chopped

2 fresh sage leaves

1 bay leaf

Sea salt and freshly ground black pepper

METHOD

For the sauce, put the tomatoes, garlic and oil in a pan, boil, reduce heat and simmer for until they cook to a pulp, crushing them occasionally

Add wine and simmer until absorbed, then add the stock, tarragon, thyme, sage, bay leaf, salt and pepper

Brush the fish with oil and season with salt and pepper

Spoon half of the sauce into a roasting tin, place the fish on top and roast in heated oven (180°C/gas 4) for 10 minutes, turn the fish over and roast for an additional 10 minutes

Place in the serving dish and keep warm

Pour the roasting juices back into the saucepan of Nicoise sauce, bring to the boil and then simmer until reduced to a pulp, add salt and pepper to taste

Pour the sauce around the fish, add the olives and fennel fronds and serve

Torta tal-lampuki

LAMPUKI PIE

The very beautiful Lampuki (or Dorado) has a silver and golden colour and is, without doubt, the island's most popular fish, especially where cooked (as here) in the traditional Lampuki pie. Lampuki season begins towards the end of August and finishes in November. When you visit Gozo, also watch out for smoked Lampuki (usually available during a plentiful season). Pilot fish are also popular, here layered with potatoes, onions, herbs and tomatoes and baked.

Pages 66 and 67 offer an additional four popular fish recipes, including swordfish, octopus, squid and the under-appreciated white bait.

INGREDIENTS

For a 15cm pie dish half the torta pastry recipe (see page 33)

1 kg of Lampuki, filleted and cut into cubes

1 onion, finely chopped

5 garlic cloves, finely chopped

12 basil leaves, finely chopped

Handful marjoram leaves, finely chopped

handful mint leaves, finely chopped

2 fresh tomatoes, roughly chopped

8 pitted green olives, roughly chopped

8 black olives, finely chopped

2tsp capers

2 medium potatoes, peeled and sliced

100ml extra virgin olive oil

Sea salt and freshly cracked pepper

METHOD

Line a 15cm pie dish with the pastry leaving pastry hanging out of the dish to form flaps

Heat a pan with the oil and sauté the onion and garlic, mix in the fish and herbs, cook for 5 minutes and stir in the olives, capers and tomatoes, continue cooking for another 5 minutes

Line the pastry with the potatoes, season the fish mixture and put on top of the potatoes

Close back the pastry flaps and cook in a moderate hot oven at 180°C for approximately 35 minutes until pastry is golden and crunchy

Leave to rest for a few minutes and serve hot.

Fanfru l-forn

BAKED PILOT FISH

INGREDIENTS

8 fillets of pilot fish cleaned and skin removed

4 potatoes, finely sliced

16 cherry tomatoes halved

2 onions finely sliced

small bunch marjoram

Small bunch parsley roughly chopped

50g breadcrumbs

8 pitted black olives, halved

2 garlic cloves finely chopped

120ml extra virgin olive oil

Sea salt and freshly cracked pepper

METHOD

Heat the oven to a temperature of 180°C

In an oven dish lay a bed of potatoes, top with the fish and sprinkle with the tomatoes, onions, herbs and olives

Finish with breadcrumbs, oil and seasoning and cook covered for about 15minutes until, potatoes and fish are cooked

Serve immediately very hot.

Qarnita fl-inbid aħmar

OCTOPUS IN RED WINE

INGREDIENTS

1kg cleaned octopus
1 litre water
1 litre red wine
10 black peppercorns
2 bay leaves

For the sauce:
1 red onion finely sliced
2 garlic cloves finely chopped
10 pitted black olives
12 cherry tomatoes, quartered
Marjoram, mint, basil, finely chopped
1 teaspoon bees honey
½ teaspoon crushed chilli
zest of 1 lime
100ml extra virgin olive oil
sea salt and freshly cracked pepper

METHOD

In a deep pan put the water, wine, peppercorns bay leaves and octopus, bring to the boil, reduce the heat and simmer for about an hour or until octopus is cooked

Remove the octopus from liquid and cut into large pieces reserving some of the liquid

In a shallow pan heat the oil and sauté the onions until golden brown, add the chilli, garlic and herbs and cook for a further minute, then add the olives and tomatoes and cook for a further 3 minutes

Finally, add the octopus, honey and lime zest, add some liquid and cook for about 10 minutes until the liquid has been reduced to the desired consistency

Season and serve.

Pixxispad

SWORDFISH AL CARTOCCIO

INGREDIENTS

4 swordfish steaks (approx. 200g each), skin removed

Zest of 1 orange

1 fennel bulb, finely sliced

4 star anise

50g pine nuts

100ml extra virgin olive oil

Sea salt and freshly cracked pepper

4 Sheets - 30cm by 30cm aluminium foil and baking paper

METHOD

Lay the four sheets of aluminium foil on the table, top each one with one sheet of baking paper

Set the fish steak in the middle of the baking paper and top with fennel, orange zest, pine nuts, seasoning and oil

Close the sides to form small purses and cook in moderate oven at 180°C for about 15minutes or on the barbeque grill for about 10 minutes

Serve the fish in their individual parcels.

Klamari bil-ful u ġobon tal-bżar

ROASTED SQUID, BROAD BEANS & CHEESE

INGREDIENTS

8 small squid, cleaned

500g shelled broad beans

80g peppered sheep cheese, grated

Juice and zest of 1 lemon

3 garlic cloves, finely chopped

½ tsp chilli flakes

15ml raspberry vinegar

small bunch of parsley, finely chopped

12 cherry tomatoes, halved

100ml extra virgin olive oil

Sea salt and freshly cracked pepper

METHOD

Cut the squid in half and using a pointed knife make criss cross cuts on the squid

Heat a pan with the oil, cook the garlic and the chilli for 30 seconds and stir in the squid and cook on high heat for 1 minute

Remove from the heat, transfer to an oven dish and mix in the lemon juice, zest, vinegar, beans, tomatoes and seasoning

Roast in a moderate oven at 180° C for about 7 minutes

Remove from oven add parsley, plate and when still hot sprinkle with the cheese leaving it to melt in the squid dish.

Meat
(Servings are for 4)

Flett tal-majjal bil-pruna u ġamm tat-tin

PAN-FRIED FILLET OF PORK WITH PRUNES & FIG JAM

Pork has been popular in Malta and Gozo for centuries and remains a staple in meat recipes to this day and is predominant in local sausages (which are often traditionally eaten raw). Here, the pork is combined with dried prunes, figs, red wine, chilli and ginger to produce a stunning dish full of aroma, flavour and texture.

For this reason, many of my regular customers order this dish for special occasions such as weddings and parties.

INGREDIENTS

1kg pork fillets cut into 2 cm pieces

12 dried prunes

75g figs jam

½ tsp chilli

75ml light bodied red wine

1 tsp thyme

A small piece fresh ginger, grated

1 green apple, skinned and sliced with core removed

60ml extra virgin olive oil

sea salt and freshly cracked pepper

METHOD

Place the pork, the prunes, jam, chilli, ginger, thyme, apple, wine and cracked pepper in a bowl and leave to marinate for at least 1 hour

Heat a pan with the oil, remove the pork from the marinade and sauté until golden on each side, add in the marinade and cook until reduced

Season and serve accompanied by boiled new potatoes.

Qarabagħli Mimli
RUFFLED STUFFED MARROWS

Gozo is famous for its marrows and no dish better illustrates their quality and flavour than this stuffed marrow recipe which incorporates many of the island's special ingredients – pork, tomato paste and cheese. Qarabagħi Mimli is a cornerstone of the Gozitan table. We have also included a dish that captures something of Gozo's modern 'take' on tradition featuring the finest quality aubergines and locally smoked sausage (any good quality sausage will also work well).

INGREDIENTS

4 small to medium marrows, cut into quarters with the flesh scooped out

extra virgin olive oil

¼ chilli, finely chopped

4 garlic cloves, finely chopped

1 medium onion, finely chopped

400g pork mince

80g tomato paste

700g potatoes, cut into slices

2 dried sheep cheese or, alternatively 100g of grated parmesan cheese

2 eggs

Sea salt and freshly ground black pepper

METHOD

Shallow fry the onions until golden brown, add half the garlic and the marrow flesh, cook for 10 minutes

Mix in the pork mince, season and cook for a further 5 minutes and let it cool completely

Now add in the beaten egg and cheese and season

Pre heat the oven to 180° C

In an oven tray layer the potatoes, season and coat with the tomato paste mixed with a little water

Place the meat mixture on top of the potatoes, cover with aluminium foil and bake for 1hr and 15 minutes

Place the marrow shells in a separate tray and brush with oil, a pinch of sea salt and freshly cracked pepper and cook in the oven for about 10 minutes

Mix some oil, chilli and garlic together and when the marrow shells are still warm brush with this marinade

Divide half the marrow shells on to 4 plates, place some pork and potato bake on top and finish off with the remaining marrow shells on top of this

Drizzle with the remaining oils and serve immediately.

Serves 4.

Brungiel u zalzett affumikat

AUBERGINE & SMOKED SAUSAGE TOWER

INGREDIENTS

400g long aubergine

2 tomatoes, sliced

2 fresh sheep's cheese, sliced

12 basil leaves

120g local smoked pork sausage, sliced

200ml extra virgin olive oil

20ml chilli oil

METHOD

Cut the aubergine into 8 chunky slices, dredge with salt and leave to stand for half an hour

Remove the salt and rinse

Heat a pan with the oil and shallow fry the aubergines until golden on each side, remove from the pan and transfer 4 pieces on a baking tray

Top each aubergine with a slice of tomato, slice of cheese, basil, sausage and repeat with aubergine, cheese and finish with basil

Bake in a moderate oven at 180°C for about 10 minutes until cheese start melting

Serve warm drizzled with chilli oil and cracked pepper.

Marvik Said, vegetable supplier, Xagħra

Fenek moqli

FREDDIE'S PAN-FRIED RABBIT WITH GARLIC & WINE

Freddie Refalo is a well-known figure on Comino Island beside Gozo during the summer months where he and son Daniel provide umbrellas and deckchairs. But Freddie is also an excellent home-cook, especially when it comes to rabbit. This is his home-fried rabbit recipe which he serves with some of the island's best, double-fried chips (an alternative is mashed potatoes mixed with fresh parsley, butter and black pepper).

The opposite page adds a twist to the cooking of rabbit with a complex blend of spices, cocoa powder and orange zest producing a dark, richly flavoured dish.

INGREDIENTS

1 rabbit cut into about 8 pieces

4 tbsp. flour seasoned with salt and pepper

4 tbsp. blended olive and sunflower oil

2 onions roughly chopped

8-10 cloves garlic, crushed with the blade of a knife or roughly chopped

250 ml white wine

6 sprigs rosemary (optional)

METHOD

Roll the rabbit pieces in the seasoned flour until lightly coated

Heat the oil in a large pan, add the rabbit, the garlic and half the onion and fry gently for 10 mins

Pour over the wine and add the rosemary (if using) and allow the wine to reduce almost completely

Continue to cook the rabbit until cooked through

Towards the end of the cooking time, add the remaining onion and gently sauté until the rabbit is fully cooked and the onions retain some crunch.

Stuffat tal-Fenek
RABBIT CASSEROLE

INGREDIENTS

1 rabbit (divided in pieces)

200g strong white flour

100cl extra virgin olive oil

2 onions peeled and sliced

4 garlic cloves crushed

2 carrots peeled and diced

5 sprigs fresh thyme

3 bay leaf

1 teaspoon mixed spice

1 tablespoon bitter cocoa powder

3 tablespoons sweet tomato paste

1 tablespoon sugar

Salt & pepper

50cl fruity red wine

210g tinned peas, drained and rinsed

Zest of two oranges (to finish the dish)

METHOD

Coat the rabbit pieces in flour seasoned with salt and pepper, shake off excess flour and put aside

Heat the oil in a deep pan, fry the onions until golden brown, add the garlic and the carrots and cook for further 4 minutes until vegetables colour

In the same pan add the floured rabbit pieces and fry until nicely browned, add the thyme, bay leaves, mixed spice and cocoa powder and toss quickly

Mix in the tomato paste and the sugar, deglaze the pan with the wine, simmer for 5 minutes and top up with water until the meat is covered

Simmer for about one and a quarter of an hour taking care that the pan does not dry out, top up with water if necessary

When the rabbit is ready and meat is cooked add the peas and cook for a further 15 minutes.

Serving suggestion: Serve the sauce separate from the meat. Serve sauce with spaghetti drizzled with zest of oranges as a starter and the rabbit accompanied by homemade fries.

Żejt taż-Żebbuġa
OLIVE OIL - GOZO'S LIQUID GOLD

Olive oil has been made since approximately 5,000BC, first in ancient Greece and then in countries such as Israel and Egypt and was introduced to the Mediterranean by the Greeks around the eight century BC. There is plenty of evidence of widespread olive production in Malta and Gozo since ancient times; archaeological finds have discovered Roman tools for olive pressing and some place names highlight its value in Maltese history and culture; two towns are named directly after the olive -Żebbug (olive) and Żejtun (oil). Widespread cultivation of olives declined when other cash crops were introduced in the early 19th century but the industry has staged something of a major comeback in recent decades and, today, some of the finest oils in the region are found here. Gozitan olive oil has a distinct, rich, fruity flavour and aroma as a result of the Islands' favourable climate and soil.

Good quality extra-virgin olive oil is rich in antioxidants that help fight bad cholesterol, contribute to reduction in risk of heart attack and cancer. Olives, olive oil and the olive leaf have all developed 'mythical' status in history, culture and well-being because of its special properties. The best oils are those that are made from hand-picked olives, pressed and bottled on the same estate – such oils are now considered in much the same way as fine wines and need to be picked at just the right time to maximise flavour and health-giving polyphenols.

Olive oil is now used widely in Gozitan cooking and on the page opposite we have included two types of pesto that show off the oil's quality and flavour.

Pesto bil-lumi u tursin
LEMON & PARSLEY PESTO

INGREDIENTS

2 bunches fresh flat leaf parsley washed and dried

The juice of 2 lemons

Salt and freshly ground black pepper to taste

125 ml of freshly grated Parmesan (or pecorino) cheese

1 large clove of garlic, finely chopped (optional)

250 ml extra-virgin Gozitan olive oil

METHOD

Finely chop the parsley

Mix the parsley with the lemon juice and the finely chopped garlic

Add sea salt and freshly ground black pepper, to taste

Add in the cheese and oil and mix well

Store in a sterilised jar in the fridge.

Makes 500 grams.

Pesto tat-tewm, ġewż u ġobon
GARLIC, WALNUT & CHEESE PESTO

In late spring and early summer, young garlic appears in profusion in Gozo and is ideal for making this flavour packed pesto which can be used in pasta, on bruschetta or simply added to a sandwich to give it that something special. The garlic can also be used in salads and other dishes.

INGREDIENTS

100g freshly picked young garlic stalks, finely chopped

50g shallot, finely chopped

50g shelled and chopped walnuts

200 ml extra-virgin olive oil

50-60g of dried Sheep's cheese or other mature hard cheese finely grated

½ - 1 teaspoon sea salt

½ teaspoon sugar

METHOD

Mix all the ingredients gently together

Depending on how coarse you like your pesto, either add the oil or place everything in a food processor and blend to the required consistency

Place in clean sterilised jars almost to the top pressing down on the pesto to eliminate air pockets

Top up with extra-virgin olive oil and refrigerate until needed

Desserts

Kikkri tal-lumi

LEMON CAPPUCCINO CUPS

This is a very stylish and easy to make dessert that will finish any meal with a flourish; half the trick is to present the dessert in separate cups for each person. They can be made in advance and kept in the fridge until needed. Enjoy the compliments.

Makes 10 small cups

INGREDIENTS

Lemon curd:
100g sugar
325ml water
32g corn flour
Zest and juice of 1 lemon
2 eggs
2 drops vanilla essence

Almond crumb base:
20g raw almonds
40g sweet biscuits
10g unsalted butter

Coffee cream:
100ml fresh cream
1 shot espresso
10g icing sugar

METHOD

Separate the egg yolks from the whites and reserve the yolks

Place the biscuits, almonds and butter together in a blender and mix until it resembles breadcrumbs

Divide this mixture between 10 cups and press slightly with the finger tips, leave to rest for half an hour

Place the water, sugar, corn flour, egg yolks, vanilla, juice and zest of half the lemon in a deep pan and mix everything together with a whisk and heat on low heat stirring constantly until it starts to bubble up

Remove from heat immediately and divide between the 10 cups and leave to cool for at least 1 hour

Whisk the cream with the icing sugar and coffee in a bowl until stiff peaks form

Using a piping bag, pipe small rosettes on each cup to form like a cappuccino froth.

Biskuttini tal-lewż
ALMOND MACAROONS

Maltese pastries come in many varieties dependent on family tradition, local custom, feast-days and special occasions. Recipes are handed on from generation to generation and, as with so much Gozitan cooking are made with fresh ingredients - orange, mandolin, lemon, clove, honey and anisette ('żanbur') or rose-water (Ilma Żahar – see page 60). These almond macaroons are an essential part of this tradition and are known as 'biskuttini tal- lewż'.

INGREDIENTS

300g raw almonds crushed plus an extra 30g for garnish

300g castor sugar

3 large egg whites

Zest of ½ lemon

Zest of ½ orange (option: 2 drops Ilma Żahar

2 rice paper

METHOD

Mix together the crushed almonds, the lemon and orange zest in a bowl

Whisk the egg whites to a stiff peak, add the sugar and whisk again until the sugar is well blended

Mix the egg white mixture carefully into the almond mixture and stir gently until all is folded well (option: add the Ilma Żahar)

Lay the rice paper on an oven tray and with the help of a piping bag fitted with a 15mm tube, pipe small disks, keeping 2cm distance between one another

On each disk put a whole almond and lightly press

Bake in preheated oven 180°C for about 10 minutes until golden, brown, cool on a wire rack and serve.

Ftira tal-ġamm
HOMEMADE JAM FTIRA

One of the secrets of good popular cooking is straightforward – use the best, freshest ingredients and keep it simple. This hugely popular dessert is Gozo's 'take' on a universal theme – quality home-made jam (whichever variety is available) and pastry filled and rolled. The smell of home-cooking and the memories come flooding back.

Warm fig tart served with caramel (or other) ice cream needs little argument – it speaks for itself.

INGREDIENTS

1 recipe ftira dough

500g fruit jam (fig, strawberry, plum, apricot etc.)

Flour for dusting

100ml extra virgin olive oil

METHOD

Open the dough on a floured surface, the size of a baking tray

Put the dough into the baking tray and spread with the desired jam, leaving a crust on the surroundings

Brush the crust with the oil, leave to rest for 10 minutes in a warm place and bake in a hot oven 240°C for about 10 minutes until crust is nicely browned and crispy

Cool on a wire rack until jam cools slightly and serve warm.

Torta tat-tin
FIG TARTE TATIN

INGREDIENTS

250g torta pastry
16 fresh purple figs, stalks removed
50g butter
100g caster sugar
50g icing sugar
1 tsp sesame seeds
30ml water

METHOD

Prepare a shallow pan that goes in the oven lined with non-stick baking paper

Heat the caster sugar with the water in a heavy based pan and cook gently until golden, remove from the heat and add the butter, stirring continuously until well incorporated

Pour in the prepared lined pan, top with the figs one near each other and sprinkle with sesame seeds

Roll out the pastry to a 2mm thickness and drape over the top of the figs making sure that the pastry seals the pan correctly

Leave to rest in a cool place for 30 minutes

Preheat oven to 200°C

Dust the tart with icing sugar and bake for approximately 25 minutes or until pastry is golden brown

Remove tart from the oven and let it cool for 2 minutes

Place a serving plate over the pastry and with a twist of the wrist; very carefully flip pan and plate over together, so that the figs face upwards, (pay special attention when handling caramelised fruit as it can be scalding)

Remove paper and serve with a caramel ice-cream.

Hawħ bl-irkotta u ġellewż

ROASTED PEACHES WITH RICOTTA & HAZELNUTS

INGREDIENTS

6 large fresh peaches

100g sugar

2 limes leaves

200g ricotta

50g icing sugar

50g shelled hazelnuts

Zest of 1 lemon

75ml fresh cream

METHOD

Roast the hazelnuts and chop them finely

Heat a deep pan and add water, sugar and lime leaves

Plunge the peaches in the water for 3 minutes, remove and refresh under cold water reserving the syrup

Peel the peaches, cut in half, remove the stone and put on a roasting tray, drizzle with some of the reserved syrup and roast in a medium hot oven at 180°C for about 10 minutes, until the peaches start getting golden brown

In a bowl mix the ricotta, icing sugar, hazelnuts, fresh cream and ½ a teaspoon of zest

To serve, fill the warm peaches with a spoon full of the ricotta mix and accompany with some of the roasted juices.

Langas fl-inbid aħmar

POACHED PEARS IN FULL BODIED RED WINE

INGREDIENTS

4 pears (if you find small Maltese June pears use 16)

50cl full bodied red wine

50g sugar

2 star anise

1 cinnamon stick

Zest and juice of 1 orange

Zest and juice of 1 lemon

50g bee's honey

METHOD

Peel the pears leaving the stem on

In a small pan, stand the pears one next to the other, top up with the wine, sugar, spices, honey, zest and juices, if the pears are not covered add some water

Simmer for 15 minutes on low heat, remove the pears from the cooking liquid and reduce the liquid by half, until the thickness of the sauce covers the spoon

Pass the sauce through a strainer and serve with the warm pears.

Ġelat tat-tadam
TOMATO ICE CREAM

Despite first reactions, this is a clever and very tasty ice-cream that will get them talking. Try it out you will be surprised. Good quality, ripe tomatoes are the order of the day.

INGREDIENTS

200g fresh tomatoes skin and seeds removed

90ml water

125ml fresh cream

50g icing sugar

8 basil leaves finely chopped

10ml extra virgin olive oil

pinch of freshly cracked pepper

Pinch of sea salt

METHOD

Drain the tomatoes well and puree with the sugar, water and oil

Beat the fresh cream to a soft peak, blend with the tomato mixture and mix smoothly until well incorporated

Add the basil, pepper and salt and mix again

Put in a container and freeze for about 6 hours giving a turn every hour

Serve sprinkled with pepper and basil or mint leaves.

Granita tar-rummien
POMEGRANATE & VERMENTINO GRANITA

Desserts that bring together the traditional and the new in stunning flavours, combinations and textures! Gozo is now producing very high quality Vermentino wine which is one of the stars of the show in the recipes that follow alongside with reliable favourites fruit, honey, lemon, spices and ginger.

INGREDIENTS

6 ripe pomegranate, gently squeezed

20cl Vermentino wine

50g caster sugar

METHOD

In a pan put the pomegranate juice with the sugar and heat until all sugar is dissolved, remove from heat and stir in the wine

Put the mixture in a flat tray and place in the freezer, whisking now and then to break the ice crystals (the end result has to be fine crystals)

Serve in Pyramid glasses.

Lumi mimli
STRAWBERRY AND GINGER CHEESECAKE IN LEMON SHELLS

INGREDIENTS

8 lemons, tops and pulp removed, keeping some of the juice

4 fresh sheep cheese

4 ginger biscuits, crushed

10g icing sugar

300g fresh strawberries, roughly chopped

16 mint leaves, finely chopped

METHOD

In a bowl mix the cheese with the ginger crumb and the sugar

Fill the lemon shells half way up with the mixture

In a separate bowl mix the strawberries with 1 tablespoon of the lemon juice and the mint leaves, top up the lemons, chill and serve.

Frott il-forn
ROASTED FRUIT

INGREDIENTS

Ingredients for the fruit roast:
1 green apple
1 pear
200g strawberries
2 peaches
40g bees honey
1 tsp fresh thyme
2 star anise
1 tsp marjoram
100ml Vermentino wine

Ingredients for the brioche :
34g milk
7g yeast
115g strong flour
7g sugar
pinch of salt
14g unsalted butter plus 40g
1 egg
4g honey
zest of half a lemon
20 golden raisins
5g cinnamon powder

METHOD

First make the brioche, melt the yeast with the warm milk and the sugar; let it stand for 15 minutes

With the help of an electric mixer fitted with a hook work all the remaining ingredients except the 40g butter until you have smooth dough

Mix in the 40g butter and work until well incorporated, cover with a damp cloth and allow to rest for 1 hour

Work again for a few seconds and divide into 5 equal pieces and shape them into buns and put on a well-greased baking tray

Let it double the size and bake at 230 degrees Celsius for 12 minutes

When ready let it cool, cut into slices, toast the pieces and serve with the fruit.

For the roasted fruit:

Wash, peel and quarter the fruits

Mix every ingredient together and disperse in an oven tray

Cook covered in a moderate oven 180°C for 30 minutes

When ready to serve, place once again in the oven uncovered until the fruit caramelises

Serve with the toasted brioche.

Mqaret

DATE ROLLS

Another hugely popular Gozitan dessert, these date rolls are best eaten fresh, perhaps with som home-made vanilla ice-cream.

INGREDIENTS

For the pastry:

200g flour

50g butter

2 tbsp. water

Extra flour for dusting

For the filling:

200g dates

2 tsp. of grated citrus peel

Pinch ground cloves

1 Tbsp. Anisette Liqueur

2 drops of Ilma Żahar

1 tbsp. sugar

50g icing sugar

Vegetable oil for frying

METHOD

Remove the pip from the dates and finely cho together with the citrus peel

Make the pastry by rubbing in the butter wit the flour; add water to form a soft dough

Put the dates in a saucepan with some wate and boil for a few minutes, until the dates ca be mashed with a fork

Stir in the citrus peel, cloves, sugar, Ilma Żaha liqueur and remove from the heat

Roll out the pastry to form a long rectangula shape about 7cm wide, spoon the filling dow the centre of the pastry, brush the visible pastr with water and fold the pastry over, ensurin that filling does not escape

Slightly flatten the pastry roll with the han and cut into diagonal shapes with a sharp knif

Heat a deep pan with the oil and deep fry th date rolls until golden brown

Drain on kitchen paper and serve warm dredge with icing sugar.

Ġbejniet bil-għasel

FRESH GOZO SHEEP'S CHEESE WITH HONEY, THYME & COFFEE

*This is one of my signature dishes that never fails to puzzle at first, amaze on tasting and delight i
sharing with others. Cheese, honey and herbs together feature in many world cuisines and with th
added texture and sharpness of the coffee beans here, it will surprise and delight – every time. Th
sheep's cheese of Gozo was made for this recipe but other similar milky cheeses will also work well.*

INGREDIENTS

4 fresh sheep cheese

120g bee's honey

Sprig of thyme, leaves removed and slightly chopped

8 Arabica coffee beans, finely ground

METHOD

Slightly warm the honey

Serve one cheeselet for each person, sprinkle
with some thyme and drizzled with honey

Finish with a dusting of coffee.

ACKNOWLEDGEMENTS

George, Hilda and Colm would like to sincerely thank all those who made this book possible; thank you for your contributions, support, enthusiasm and criticisms. In particular, we would like to thank:

Mark Agius and Dwardu Spiteri (Dwardu's butchers, Sannat)

Jeannette Bajada

Maria Assunta and Lawrence Bajada (Ilma Żahar, Xaghra)

Andrew Busuttil, Marita Sciberras, Vincienne Xuereb, Steve Mifsud, Luke Theuma and Mary Louise Fiteni (Connection Caterers)

Anthony and Lina Grech

Omar, Tony, Agnes, Marcello and Melanie Grech

Daniel Magrin (D Venue Restaurant, Xaghra)

David and Lina Mercieca (David's Bakery)

Freddie Refalo and Maria Galea

Abraham Said and Daniel Sultana (Abraham's Supplies)

Marvik Said

George Scicluna (CVC)

Joe and Marnèse Spiteri (Ta' Mena Estate)

Philip Spiteri (Kartell Restaurant)

Blodwen Spiteri (Gutenberg Press)

Henry and Martha Vella

Marco Vella (Attard & Co.)

Carmel Rapa (Ta' Mena Winery)

Mario Galea (fresh Gozo Cheese, Gharb)

Very special thanks also to Claire Borg for her excellent photography and also to Tony Daly, Dylan Creane, Ciara Regan, George Scicluna and Joe Spiteri.

As ever, thanks to Dylan Creane for his ongoing design support and input.

Finally, very special thanks to Stephanie and Hilda

INDEX

Sheep's Cheese with Honey Thyme & Coffee Beans, 92

Spaghetti

    with Lemon Basil & Parsley, 50

    with Local Sausage & Mushrooms, 56

    with Prawns, Chilli, Lemon & Rocket, 52

    with Raw Mediterranean Tomato Sauce, 51

Strawberry & Ginger Cheesecake in Lemon Shells, 88

Stuffed Tomatoes with Aubergine, 34

Stuffed Tomatoes with Mushrooms & Artichoke Hearts, 35

Swordfish Al Cartoccio, 67

Tagliatelle with Baby Calamari & Artichoke, 49

Tomato & Melon Soup, 7

Ice Cream, 86

Traditional Soup, 9

Tomato Sauces

    Green Tomato Sauce, 47

    Ketchup, 55

    Raw Tomato Sauce, 47

    Tomato Sauce normally served with Pasta, 46

    Traditional Tomato Sauce served with Ravioli, 46

Torta, Basic Pastry Recipe, 33

Wine, 36-41

Secretly, she'd her mind.

It happened sometime between two and three o'clock after he'd taken off his shirt. On a good day Ben was hard to resist. On a day like today with the afternoon sun beating down on his broad back as he worked on her house—resistance was futile.

And why had she been resisting him?

'You mind if I get cleaned up before we move on to the office work? I could use a shower.'

Instantly Hilary had processed the statement and kicked into analysis mode. Ben was going to take a shower, but there wasn't a 'You want to join me?' invitation in his eyes. Chance of sex: ten per cent.

Hilary said in her best 'of course I'm not thinking carnal thoughts' voice, 'Sure. Be my guest.'

Ben brought in some clothes from his truck and then the torture began. First he closed the bathroom door, but she didn't hear it click. Did she dare join him? Next there was the sound of water bombarding her with images of his strong, naked, taut body.

Following her urges, she went towards the bathroom. She could do this, of course she could. Chance of sex: eighty per cent. Just as she chucked her T-shirt, the water turned off.

Damn.

Chance of sex: nought per cent. But the night was still young.

Dear Reader,

When my editor invited me to write for THE
WRONG BED series, we brainstormed all the
places where beds were found. I wanted to do
something a little different—write a book about a
place with a veritable treasure trove of beds: a
mattress company. Immediately I thought of one
of my favourite Broadway musicals, *Once Upon a
Mattress*, based on the fairy tale *The Princess and
the Pea*. But you know the thing about fairy tales?
They're always about the princess and never
about the prince. Does that seem fair? Not to me.
Every princess may have her day, but every
prince has his story, and Ben was Hilary's prince.

Hilary was so easy for me to write. I knew her
pain and the distrust that always seemed to
follow. Ben was more difficult. Oh, he was a
prince, all right, but his world wasn't *quite* the
way he assumed it to be.

So, on to the story. I love to hear from readers, so
please visit my website at
www.kathleenoreilly.com.

Enjoy!

Kathleen O'Reilly

ONCE UPON A MATTRESS

by

Kathleen O'Reilly

MILLS & BOON®

This book is dedicated to the most disagreeable girl.
May she always be so contrary.

*First published in Great Britain 2004
by Harlequin Mills & Boon Limited,
Eton House, 18-24 Paradise Road, Richmond, Surrey TW9 1SR*

© Kathleen Panov 2003

ISBN 0 263 84004 2

21-0304

*Printed and bound in Spain
by Litografía Rosés S.A., Barcelona*

1

BEN MACALLISTER STUDIED her from across the conference room table. "Bad breakup?"

"I beg your pardon?" she replied, lifting her head.

Hilary Sinclair wasn't the sort of woman that men would notice at first glance. At first glance, a man might overlook her—dismiss her even. The second time, Ben had noticed the "I'm bookish" stiffness—the social difficulty that came from being highly intelligent.

The third glance turned his head and made him wonder why the world didn't pay more attention to Hilary Sinclair. He settled back in his chair, the old wood squeaking under his weight. "I don't mean to be rude, but you're very hostile toward younger men and you certainly aren't happy."

Ben was new to his father's company—MacAllister Beds—but Hilary was even newer. Ten days ago she'd come on board, and it was only in the past week that he'd begun to analyze her.

"You've sat around and contemplated what you've assumed is the absolute misery of my love life, and you've divined all this in the short time since I've started?" she asked, leveling her green gaze at him as if he was the scourge of the earth, which in a perverse way proved his theory.

"I'm intelligent, not completely understanding of the workings of the female mind, but I think that's an impossibility. So, to answer your question, yes."

"A woman must have a man to be happy. Is that what you think?" Her eyes flashed and came alive. He liked it when she was angry.

"No, but it doesn't hurt."

She arched a dark brow, not quite as well as he could, but the intent was there. "You're absolutely right. And if you must know, I castrated him." Then she took a sip from her Starbucks coffee cup, two drops leaking onto her shirt. She didn't even notice, just put down her cup and stared determinedly at the blank sheet of paper in front of her.

He didn't believe her for a moment, but protective male instincts made him press his legs together.

The conference room was quiet, the rain drumming on the old roof of the warehouse. He'd shown up early, to be prompt for what might be an important meeting, but also because he knew she'd be early, too.

Oddly enough, he found himself compelled to talk to her, compelled to garner her attention. "You know, I think I watched a movie about you on Lifetime."

She lifted her head again. "Very funny. If you don't mind, I don't think the workplace is the proper forum for a conversation on my personal life."

Ben shrugged. "I was curious, that was all."

She tapped her pen on the long wooden table, not meeting his eyes. "Why did your father invite you to the product launch meeting? I wasn't aware that the Director of Security would be involved."

Ben winced, and he was sure she noticed. "With Sylvia's broken leg, I think my dad wants everyone to pitch in and help cover for her. *Even* Security," he added, more sarcastically than necessary, which ruined any effort at a nice recovery.

Director of Security, my ass. Being offered the gimme position had been a low blow, but he could prove to his father that he'd underestimated him.

He'd come back to Dallas to help his family out, thought that maybe he could make a difference. MacAllister Beds had never been Ben's idea of excitement, but this time he was determined to sweat it out. He'd never cared much about the company; his family was the reason he was here instead of completing number thirty-seven on his "list of things to do before I die."

"So you're going to work on the product launch?" she asked, either overlooking his sarcasm or else not noticing it. He'd bet good money it was the latter.

"If I'm needed, sure." The new Dreamscape line was scheduled for product launch at the ISPA trade show in Las Vegas three months from now. Ben had hoped to be a part of the project.

She nodded coolly and stared back at the paper, dismissing him.

But he wasn't ready to be dismissed. Yet. "The new mattress is ready to go?"

"Certainly," she said.

He wanted to ask more questions, ask how many lines were on that yellow legal page, ask her if she hated all men, or should he take it personally. Before he could annoy her further, his father walked in, and that was Ben's cue to sit back and watch. Ben took out his notes for the meeting, not sure what he'd be doing, but he still wanted to be prepared.

Ben's father was the undisputed head and Ben's brother, Allen, was the heir apparent to MacAllister Beds.

MacAllister Beds, the last bed you'll ever buy.

Too bad MacAllister marriages didn't last as long as their mattresses.

Ben clenched his folder a little tighter.

Martin MacAllister sat down at the end of the conference table, situating his big frame into the old chair. His brown hair—the same light shade as Ben's—had just now started to turn gray, but his dark eyes were full of humor and youth. He settled back, sighing in relief when he finally got comfortable.

Allen trundled in, late as usual, then sat down at their father's right hand.

Martin MacAllister put on the bifocals that Ben knew

he hated and looked at his meeting agenda. "Ben, glad you could join us. Got big plans today?"

"I thought I'd write some new security procedures," he answered, almost as a joke.

"Procedures, huh? Good, good. Let's get started, shall we?"

And for the next forty-five minutes, Ben might as well have been wallpaper. His father asked Hilary all sorts of questions about the launch, what time the press conference was scheduled, what media contacts they had, shipping timetables and meeting plans.

And absolutely nothing about security at all.

Ben carefully took his notes and folded them into a paper airplane.

He could be in Colorado right now, breathing fresh mountain air at the J&D ranch, number thirty-seven on his list of things to do before he died. But he'd put that off, because he thought it was important to be here—for the company, for his family.

He almost laughed.

While the others were occupied doing real work, he got up and walked to the windows. For a while he simply stared out of the diamond panes at the modern gray lines and squares that made up the skyline of downtown Dallas. He was slowly going out of his mind.

The constant drumming of the rain on the roof should have been relaxing, but instead his knee got stiff. The same knee he'd broken when he was working as a ski instructor in the Alps.

Absently he rubbed the stubborn ligament. He had thought coming back home would be the right thing to do. Helping out his mother and father, easing their burden while they went through such a painful divorce. Only, apparently, no one else thought it was a painful divorce.

For once he'd thought he could come back and help, take the painful job and try to pick up the pieces. But everyone in his family seemed smiling and cheerful, as if nothing had happened.

Everyone except Ben.

MARTIN MACALLISTER SAT DOWN in the chair across from his son, his glasses slipping on his nose. "You wanted to see me, Ben?"

His father didn't look distressed; on the contrary, he looked more relaxed than he had been in years. Ben rubbed the ache at his temples and settled back behind his desk, remembering his purpose. "Yes. I want to do more with the product launch. Maybe I could coordinate, or manage, or just help."

Martin frowned, which was a bad sign. "You do?"

"Well, yes," Ben answered.

The room was silent, only the whirring of the air conditioner and then finally a long, painful squeak as his father shifted in the heavy chair. "I'm sorry. Sure, we'll think of something. Glad you called me in here. I've been meaning to ask your advice."

At last. Ben nearly sighed in relief. Instead he put on his serious I'm-listening face. "Yes?"

"You remember that fall you went to Alaska as a fishing guide? I've been thinking about going up there. Just me and the halibut, alone in the great outdoors."

Running away. His father wanted to run away. *Classic.* "It's a lot of fun, Dad, and I know that with what you're going through now—"

"What?"

"The divorce."

"Oh, no. I'm fine. Got a lunch date with your mom on Wednesday. We need to put the house on the market."

What?

Ben struggled for calm. No, for today, he would be productive, happy, at peace. According to his sister-in-law, Dr. Tracy MacAllister—the Love Doctor—he should put his anger behind him. Not that he put much stock in her advice. You'd think she could have stopped her in-laws' divorce if she wasn't such a quack.

Ben's voice sounded completely normal when he asked why.

"It's too big for just your mother and I'm going to get a Winnebago."

Ben closed his eyes. The company had been in Dallas for eighty-three years. Three generations of Mac-Allisters and no telling how many mattresses had been passed through these walls. And now his father wanted to buy a motor home. "What about the company?"

"I've got some ideas."

Ideas. Ben knew lots about ideas. Ideas were dangerous. Ben opened his eyes, but the pain still throbbed in his head. "What sort of ideas, Dad?"

"Nothing for you to worry about. Imagine this instead. In a couple of years, we'll be out shooting wild game in Africa together. Bang...bang." Martin's watch alarm sounded. "Whoops. Got a meeting with Hilary to go over a couple more details on the new line. Great lady. Lots of potential. See ya, son." He stopped in the doorway. "And remember, if you need anything, just ask. We're all here for you." Then his father disappeared.

Ben stared, wondering who the man was that had just left. *Wild game in Africa?* Hell, his father fainted at the sight of blood.

He paced around his small office, hands locked behind his back. So what was he supposed to do? If his father thought he wasn't capable of helping out, his father was wrong.

No, he'd do this Director of Security thing, even if it killed him.

It was only a first step, and not a big one at that. Time to return to the family. Not that anyone seemed to notice that he'd been missing, of course.

Ben went back to the safety of his desk and popped two aspirin. Where to start?

He took the folder from the top of his desk and read the computer printout of the staff's Internet access reports. There seemed to be widespread page views of *Playboy* on the fourth floor, and there was some dating instruction viewage on the third floor. Ben laughed. He should check into that. It wasn't like security at Fort Knox, but there just wasn't a lot going on.

The aspirin started kicking in, and he felt strong enough to tackle the more mundane part of the job. He tugged open his desk drawer and pulled out a book. *Hacking Exposed: Network Security Secrets & Solutions.*

He opened the book to the first page. Chapter 1. Casing the Establishment.

By page fifteen, he was ready for an afternoon nap. He locked his hands behind his head and eased back in his chair, studying the walls. Maybe he could patch up the spidery cracks that ran near the ceiling, then at least he'd have something to do.

He'd worked for a roofer in St. Thomas one year. Item number four—one summer in the Caribbean. Check. Ah, that had been the perfect place. While hammering away at the flat roofs of the villas, he'd had a hard time looking away from the crystal blue waters that sparkled as far as the eye could see.

Not like Dallas, where the five-day forecast this week was rain, rain, and more rain.

He shouldn't be daydreaming. He should check out

that Internet site. He clicked on his mouse and pulled up the page.

Top ten pickup lines. Ben started to laugh as he read.

"Hey, baby, do you believe in love at first sight, or do you want me to walk in again?"

Gag. Too clichéd. He could do better than that. He thought for a minute.

"Do I have a chance in hell with you? Don't tell me if I don't because I just gotta try," he said to himself.

He never heard the person entering his office; he just had the feeling someone was behind him.

Ben clicked on the word-processing icon, but it was too late. He looked behind him.

Busted.

By Hilary Sinclair.

She smiled tightly, her lips curving in a smug manner.

Ben was quick—threw himself into things right from the start—but when she looked at him as if he didn't belong here, it really ticked him off. One thing about Miss Sinclair, she knew mattresses. One thing about Ben, he didn't.

To make matters worse, she wore this dark shade of lipstick that should have looked goth, but instead it looked inviting.

"May I help you," he asked, not thinking about her mouth.

"Busy, Mr. MacAllister? Didn't want to interrupt."

Ben started typing away in the word processor.

"Clearing my train of thought. Humor is an excellent stimulus when your cerebral cortex is overutilized."

She pursed her midnight-dark mouth and her eyes narrowed. "Is that true?"

"No."

Her green eyes narrowed even further. They were cat eyes, tilted at the corner, and now they were mere slits. "Your father asked that you help out with the travel arrangements for the team. I've put together everyone's itineraries, and their airline requests."

Ben's headache returned. Travel agent was *not* on his list of things to do.

She tossed her long dark hair back from her face. She had the kind of hair that kinked in the wet weather, and now that he thought about it, it'd pretty much perpetually kinked since the first day she started at MacAllister Beds. That's what ten days of solid rain did to hair.

Why did he let her get under his skin? Ben's emotional Richter scale was usually on low to very low, but she spiked the needle, both in a figurative and literal sense.

Perhaps charm and a little bit of ignorance were in order. He could do both well. "Do we know what hotel to book?"

"The show is at the Paris Las Vegas. We'll do the press conference there, as well."

Ben jotted it down on his notepad. "Airline?"

"Iberia."

He looked up. She didn't crack a mandible muscle. Ben stood his ground. For a long time she stared him down. What she didn't know was that he'd spent six months as a bouncer during his Stanford years. And that gave him the upper hand. Finally she broke. "That was a joke," she mumbled.

"Yes, I'm sure it was. Airline?"

"Whatever's cheapest. We'll be flying out on Sunday evening, although Allen has asked for a Saturday flight because he wants to gamble. Your father wants to rent a motorcycle and ride around Vegas while he's there, and I'll be happy with whatever arrangements you make."

"Window or aisle?"

"I beg your pardon?"

"Would you and Allen like a window or the aisle?"

"Aisle."

"Special dietary needs." He quirked a brow, a blatant show-off gesture.

"I'd like a plate without processed meat."

"Vegetarian?"

"No, thank you. Vegetables don't agree with me."

"Perhaps I could pack a peanut butter and jelly sandwich? It might be gentler on your system."

She took a deep breath, her rumpled blouse rising and falling. In, out, in, out. His eyes followed her breathing, and damned if he wasn't getting hard.

"Sarcasm is unbecoming in a professional environment," she said, and he wondered if she'd think hard-ons were unbecoming.

Instead, he cleared this throat. "And I thought I was being considerate."

"Shall I assume this task is not beyond your capabilities and that you can work it into your—" she shot a glance at his monitor "—busy schedule?"

Her voice was full of rebuke, as if she were a schoolteacher correcting a wayward student. Ben had never indulged in schoolteacher fantasies, but images popped into his brain—images that could get him in trouble with Hilary Sinclair.

For a moment he contemplated her prickliness. She wasn't his type, not to imply that he limited himself to a type, but she had something that appealed to him. Here was someone clearly in need of a life adjustment. She didn't smile enough, didn't look happy at all. He'd never seen a woman more in need of rescuing than Hilary Sinclair.

And Ben, who'd never rescued anything in his life, was captivated.

Life was too short to ignore such heaven-sent opportunities. "I like your blouse, Miss Sinclair," he said.

Finally, success. He was rewarded with a deep flush. Deep and decadent. In quite a disordered manner, the rigid Miss Sinclair pulled a tin from her pocket and popped an Altoids in her mouth, and then, remembering her manners, put the box on his desk.

Ben didn't look at the tiny mints; instead he was fascinated by her curves. She had been all tight lines, straight back, narrow eyes, but now, as if by magic, her cheeks were rounded, almost plump, her eyes wide and liquid. She had the guilty look of a woman who'd been caught in the wrong bed.

Ben idly traced the rim of the desk with his index finger, imagining what lay underneath that rumpled white blouse. There was nothing like crossing the line to make things interesting. His smile grew wider, his hard-on harder.

"I need to leave," she said, turning tail to run.

He watched the crinkled skirt as she rushed out the door.

"Oh, Miss Sinclair?"

She turned and leaned against his door frame, panic in those wonderful cat's eyes. "What?"

"You forgot your mints."

2

HILARY HAD NEVER liked wet spots. They were uncomfortable, unsightly and could lead to early onset of mildew. She stared up at her ceiling and watched the wet spot grow larger. Outside, the storms were raging, and inside apprehension was swelling, right along with the wet spot.

She turned on the radio, hoping to block out the internal turmoil. The soothing tones of Dr. Tracy, the Love Doctor, filled the air.

"Next caller."

"Hello, Dr. Tracy, I've been having problems with my boyfriend..."

Boyfriend? It was such an innocent-sounding word. Hilary had had a boyfriend once, and she and Mark had encountered no problems. Of course, he *had* broken off their seven-year engagement, which some might consider to be a problem.

She liked to think of it as a blessing.

Now she was footloose and fancy-free, and if she really put her mind to it, she could do footloose and fancy-free. Yup, she was on her way to a new and improved lifestyle.

And any second now, her new and improved life-style was going to spring a leak.

Cursing her Realtor, she moved the rugs out of the way and stared at the slightly warped, wooden flooring beneath.

She had thought the softened appearance gave it character. She was a moron.

Hilary didn't like insecurity. She knew she was capable and intelligent, a real go-getter. Yet, this afternoon when Ben MacAllister had flashed her a bit of his oh-so-abundant charm, she'd had a tremendous desire to go out and get her nails done.

Men like him didn't notice women like her. He had charisma, was handsome and she'd heard the stories about all the places he'd been.

So why pay attention to her?

Inconceivable. No mere man would reduce her to such a quivering mass of spineless Jell-O. And thanks to Mark, men weren't to be trusted—none of them, not one bit.

While she was contemplating her own gullibility, the first drop fell. Big and fat.

Hilary dashed to what was someday going to be her newly remodeled kitchen and searched frantically for a bucket. There, back at the far wall under the sink, she found the shiny blue plastic pail she'd salvaged from Mark's place in Atlanta. She carried it back to the living room and, feeling rather cocky, placed it under what was now a steady stream of water. Then she put her hands on her hips, ready to battle the storm gods.

Take that.

It would require more than a puny drip-drip to poke holes in her future.

She dusted off her hands and sank down in front of the spot where the TV would eventually go. She couldn't afford a TV yet—Mark had taken theirs in the breakup.

Twenty-seven inches, right there in front of the bay window. Twenty-seven inches in approximately ten days—as soon as she got her first paycheck from MacAllister Beds, thank you very much.

She listened as Dr. Tracy calmly explained to her caller that she was kidding herself about her new boyfriend. That he would never amount to anything and the caller should dump him.

Sage advice. So thrilling to be the dumper rather than the dumpee. So where had Dr. Tracy been when Hilary was in Atlanta?

In Dallas, of course.

That was Hilary's home now, but it didn't feel like it. Yet.

She loved her new house, she really did. It was situated in Kessler Park, a small suburb just south of Dallas. The house was small, like Mark's house back in Atlanta. It had wooden floors that, when polished and disinfected, had a fresh, pine scent. Okay, perhaps it was a *lot* like Mark's house, but this new and improved house had three little rooms rather than four. Living room, kitchen and, as soon as she moved all the boxes, she'd even have a bedroom. Of course, it did need a little work. But she was willing to do whatever it took to start over.

A new life, a new house.

Then she took a hard look at the ceiling and sighed. And a new roof.

She thought about calling the roofer, even went and picked up the phone, but then she thought of what repairmen charged these days. Her credit card was in a world of hurt. No, she thought as she put down the phone. She'd wait out the storm, wet spot and all. Again she studied her ceiling. Really, it didn't look *that* bad. If she were lucky, the storm would pass soon.

Thunder boomed and she jumped, still a little nervous about being alone. What she needed was company. She went to her would-be bedroom, rummaged through the boxes until she found the old paper box that she had treasured since her childhood. She popped open the lid and at last pulled out her friend, her confidant, her constant. The storms raged around her, and Hilary held tight to her musty, yet still pristinely preserved, stuffed Benjamin Franklin doll.

When your father was in the air force, some guy in a red cape and the likes of Barbie just didn't cut it. Thomas Jefferson, Betsy Ross, John Wayne—those were the stuff of legends.

She padded back to the living room, feeling a little

better with Benjamin at her side. This was the first time she'd truly been on her own, and although she was off to a shaky start, things would work out.

She hoped.

Hilary stared at the wise man sitting in her lap. *Of course they will, won't they, Ben?*

If only it would stop raining.

An ominous creaking sounded deep in the bowels of her roof.

She didn't want to see this.

Crack.

That made her look. One truss jutted right through the middle of her ceiling, drywall drooping like a weeping willow. Above that, there was only the dark gray sky.

And of course, rain.

Her mother had always punished her for cussing—a lady never cusses—but this time Hilary swore up and down in a manner that her father, retired Air Force Colonel Douglas Sinclair, would have approved of.

Just for good measure, she swore again.

Benjamin stared back at her, his blue eyes laughing at her behind his wire-frame spectacles.

"You keep that up, I'll put you back in the box."

She found the first water-removal ad in the yellow pages and picked up the phone to dial.

But there was no dial tone.

Unbelievable.

BEN SHUFFLED through the papers on his desk, not that it helped. Nine at night, and he hadn't made it through the first diagram yet. The internals of a bed. He had been an English major, not an engineer.

The Cowboys game on TV called to him. *Ben, you don't really want to read that, do you? Come watch me.*

Why did football have to have such a seductive voice? He groaned and took another sip of his cola.

No, he was not going to accept defeat at the hands of an innerspring. He propped his elbows on his desk and tried to concentrate.

Not that it helped.

MacAllister Beds wasn't about security, it was about a mattress. And if Ben was going to succeed here, he really needed to understand how a mattress was put together.

He blew out a breath, staring at the springs.

What the hell was a helical anyway?

AFTER A THOROUGH CHECK of her closets for ax murderers, Hilary knew the dead phone line was not a plan to kill her, merely another step to wrecking her new and improved life.

With half a tank of gas, she wasn't going far, and gas stations open in Kessler this late at night were hard to find. She found a hotel nearby, a by-the-hour establishment, but decided against it.

At two in the morning, she found her way to the familiar confines of MacAllister Beds.

Thank God. Tired and exhausted, she was ready to discover if the company's advertising claims were true.

The office was dark and gloomy, shadows creeping along the wall. Hilary clutched her herbal-extracts pillow to her chest, letting the scents of lavender and barley soothe her senses. Her backpack was filled with tomorrow's clothes, toiletry bag, mini-alarm clock, one breakfast bar and a new tin of mints. Only two more days until the weekend. Thank God. Maybe she could spend the time waterproofing her house.

The rain pounded, but there were no drip-drip-whoosh sounds of a roof about to collapse, merely the rather loud whirring of the ancient air-conditioning system.

The Future Products and Research Testing area was on the third floor, and she was relieved to see the old metal elevator waiting for her. They had said she could have after-hours access—anything to keep their workers happy and productive. Right now, Hilary was too exhausted to think about work. Just a few hours of sleep was all she needed, and the research testing area was the perfect place.

The elevator shuddered to a halt, and she slid back the iron gate. First she looked to make sure the hallway was empty, and then she crept toward the open glass doorway that housed the next generation of Mac-Allister Beds.

At last.

Inside was another long hallway lined with eight

doors. Each room housed a bed, a small television set, a nightstand, and a small hospital-style bathroom. Not quite the comforts of home, but there were no leaks, no standing water, and best of all, no room charges.

Hilary wandered from room to room, examining each bed closely. Over the years, she'd learned the power of a good mattress.

Five years ago she had graduated from the University of Tampa with a degree in industrial engineering. First job out, and she started in the sleep products industry. Twelve months later, she'd discovered she loved it, even with the uninvited remarks from the occasional yuckster: sleeping on the job, or sleeping with her boss. Everyone thought they were comedians.

She finally settled on the last room at the end of the hallway, number eight. First, she set her alarm for five o'clock—didn't want to get caught. Next, she bounced on the mattress for a moment, then kicked off her shoes and sank onto the bed.

Ah. Bliss.

For a long time, she stared at the ceiling, wondering about her roof, wondering about her job, wondering about her $9,337 Visa balance, but gradually the lavender did its job, the barley cleared her worries away, and Hilary fell into a deep sleep.

BEN LIFTED HIS HEAD off his desk and opened one eye, the morning light way too bright in his office. Immediately the hammer in his head pounded with a vengeance. Ouch. Why in a building full of beds had he chosen to fall asleep at his desk?

"Mr. MacAllister!" It was the voice of a drill sergeant.

And now he was wide-awake. His latest temporary secretary, Helga Von Schmidt, was punctual, efficient and possessed no visible sense of humor. He hated her.

"Security registered motion detection in the testing center last evening and no trials were scheduled. I thought you might want to know, as security is your job." She lifted one dark eyebrow as if he were completely inept. James Bond he wasn't, but for God's sake, it was a mattress factory. What were they going to steal?

"I'm on the case, Helga. You can relax now."

She humphed and stalked out the door without so much as a cheerful smile to start the day. Ben wondered if the temporary agency would be annoyed if he called and requested a new secretary.

Probably. He seemed to be annoying a lot of people lately.

Still, security was his job. Or at least his latest job.

And it was time to check out the facts. Down at the research center, Ben looked into each room, wondering if he should test for fingerprints.

Nah. By the time he entered room number eight, he knew that no fingerprints were necessary.

There was a new smell that permeated this room. Pleasant, comforting. Not at all what they normally used in the testing lab, where antiseptic deodorizer was de rigueur.

The bed looked completely unused, and yet...

He sat down on the bed, a new test unit for the Dreamscape line. The innersprings gave way just as they'd been designed. He leaned back, letting the warm smell wash over him. Without thinking, he rested his head on the pillow, the scent of, what was that smell? Something with flowers and something else. It was soothing, relaxing, yet oddly elusive.

Something sharp poked his spine and he reached behind him, looking for a clue. But there was nothing.

Someone had lain here, he was sure of it. But why? A little catnapping on the job, or a little catnapping on the side?

What a perfect setup for an affair. No hotels necessary, just use the company's product.

Ben sat up. For the first time the weight of responsibility was resting on his shoulders. With a scowl that would have made Helga proud, he strode out of the room.

Tonight he would discover just exactly what was being researched in the testing center.

Or who.

3

BEN WANDERED through the hallways late into the night, hoping he looked like the proprietary owner rather than a paranoid Director of Security. No one seemed to think it strange that Ben, who never worked more than thirty hours a week before, was now stalking the halls like a man bent on worldwide domination.

That was a laugh. All he wanted was his family back together.

Worldwide domination was probably easier. Actually, getting his family back together looked pretty much impossible. His mom acted too accepting of the divorce, his father was ready to audition for *Fear Factor*. MacAllister Beds was all that was left.

Gradually, the plant had emptied, the parking lot vacated. Now it was time.

He went to the research center and picked his spot carefully. The bed across from room number eight.

It sounded like a bad cable movie. Typical Thursday night fare.

He shook his head, tossing the thought aside, then he shut off the lights. Instantly, the room turned black as pitch, empty. He settled himself on the bed, crossing his arms across his chest.

Eleven...midnight. Still nothing. He tossed on the mattress, wishing for the familiar bed in his apartment. Another storm raged outside, the cooling masses pressing against the heated air. Nothing to worry about.

Finally, convinced he *was* paranoid and all was actually right with the world, Ben fell asleep, dreaming of lavender and the green eyes of a cat.

DETERMINED TO HAVE a solid alibi, Hilary decided to work in her office until midnight, or until her body quit, whichever came first. To be honest, the world was getting a little hazy and she wasn't exactly sure what was what.

Could be the early onset of a cold. She should have stocked up on Vitamin C.

She made due with two cold tablets sans water. Her throat had expanded and she wasn't sure that the water would have gone down. Her voice had dropped two octaves since this afternoon and soon it would be gone altogether. She liked talking to herself as her voice disintegrated—pretending she was Mae West. After all, a woman needed role models.

Feeling a little giddy, she did a short bump and grind to get into her sleep shirt and shorts.

By the time she reached the third floor, she was pretty well wiped. Walking like the zombie she was, she thought she'd returned to the room she'd been in the night before. Pulling her pillow from her backpack, she inhaled the soothing barley with a heavy sigh. At least she could still breathe.

She collapsed on the bed and then climbed under the crisp sheets. Her eyes felt so heavy, sleep was so close. Thank God for MacAllister Beds.

THERE WAS A HAND on her breast. A possessive hand. Hilary smiled drowsily at the familiar warmth. Mark always did have a perfect sense of timing.

The alarm began to beep, and Hilary reached over to shut it off.

Then she rolled closer to him, basking in the heat that radiated from him. Ah...he felt so good. Slowly her fingers crept underneath his pajama shirt to find hard muscles beneath.

It must be the gym. She had told him it would pay off.

His lips trailed over her neck, and she could smell his new cologne. It was milder than what he usually wore, but underneath she could smell him. Strong, bold, masculine.

She tried to open her eyes, but she felt too lazy, too adored. Diving into this warm pool of hedonism, Hilary simply let him dally at her neck. Never had she felt so hot. It was like fire everywhere his lips touched.

She wrapped her arms around him, bringing him fully on top of her. With a contented sigh, she absorbed his weight, his strength. Her hands splayed over his back, over his butt. There she lingered, wondering why she had never noticed exactly how built he was.

Tomorrow she would tell him. Or today. Maybe she could tell him yesterday. Oh, she was getting silly.

Then his lips took hers in a kiss that gave no quarter. She had never let him kiss her before she had brushed her teeth, but today she didn't want to move. Didn't want to leave this marvelous world where kissing was so much fun.

And soon she was responding to his kiss and forgot all about her morning breath. It felt amazing to just live in the moment.

He pushed up her shirt, and she felt cool air against her overheated flesh. But soon his hands were there, hard and daring.

Everywhere they touched her, she responded. It was as if she was new, unfamiliar.

His hands cupped her breasts, and his fingers stroked her eager nipples. She arched her back, wanting more of his ardent attention. The air felt thick and heavy, the blackness like a balm. All was quiet, except for the sound of his breath. Steady and strong.

She felt detached from her body, the sensations so intense that she could no longer separate each new touch.

His hips pressed against her and she moaned. A heavy ache beat like a pulse between her thighs. Feel-

ing very Mae, she wrapped her legs around him and
ground her hips tight.

THE LINE BETWEEN reality and his dream was getting all
blurred now. Ben's logical brain was shouting for him
to wake up. His primordial brain had abandoned all
principles and just wanted more.

Her hands were not shy at all, exploring his chest
and his stomach with a sureness that made him burn.
She was a flame that he held in his arms; everywhere
she touched, his skin turned to fire.

And against his neck, her lips whispered a promise
of paradise.

He could smell her, smell the lavender, the barley,
the musky arousal that even her perfume could not
mask.

Her magic fingers unbuttoned his fly and then slid
beneath his briefs, and she laughed, low and husky.
"Mark," she whispered against his neck, as if just his
name delighted her.

Mark?

Mark?

Ben opened his eyes and stared into wanton green
eyes that glowed fever-bright with desire.

He had tasted the heat of her lips. He had felt her
breasts heavy in his hands. Still, her voice played in his
head.

Mark?

With legs slightly unsteady, Ben ignored all his instincts, climbed out of the bed and turned on the lights. The sight of her bare golden skin was mesmerizing. His stubble had left red streaks on her skin. Marks of possession.

Ben wasn't a man who thought in terms of possession, hell, he prided himself on having as few as possible, but this morning there it was. His mark.

He could do nothing but stare, his body protesting the space between them. He was a fool.

The fog lifted from her gaze and her face froze in horror. "Mr. MacAllister," she gasped, pulling her shirt down and gathering the covers around her. She looked the picture of naive innocence. Ben remembered the way she had stroked him earlier and thought the Victorian modesty bit was way overdone.

"I think you can call me Ben," he said with what he hoped was a reassuring smile. Unfortunately, her eyes flashed sexual harassment. What was the law, anyway?

She pulled the sheet tight around her, an extra layer of protection over her shirt and shorts. "Let's just forget this moment ever happened. Now if you'll excuse me, I'll get dressed."

Oh, please. "You are dressed," he said in a calm, non-threatening voice. "Look, this was nothing more than a case of mistaken identity."

She tried to climb out of the bed, but the sheet kept coming untucked, and she wouldn't let go. He held a hand, but she scooted away from him. "Don't touch me."

As if he were some sort of monster. Jeez, who had climbed into bed with whom here? And why was she here? "Look, I'm sorry. Okay? But this isn't that big a deal."

She swung her legs over the side of the bed and stood. Then she braced a hand behind her on the bed and closed her eyes. For a second he thought she was going to faint. But not Miss Hilary Sinclair. She opened her eyes again, emerald sharp, and took a deep breath. "Not a big deal? You are *such* a man."

He jammed his hands into his pockets. "A fact you were perfectly happy with about fifteen minutes ago."

Direct hit. Her faced flushed fire-engine red. "I expect a co-worker to behave with a bit more decorum, but obviously in your case, that's too much to ask. And now, if you'll excuse me, I'm leaving."

She shuffled out the door with quite a bit of dignity for a woman sporting humidity hair, dragging a sheet behind her.

BEN SPENT the early-morning hours locked in his office, waiting for a decent hour to make a call. Tonight, when he had a cold beer in his hand and a cold shower nearby, he would linger over the surprising aggressiveness of Miss Hilary Sinclair and her bodacious breasts, but right now he needed to put MacAllister

Beds first. He picked up the phone and dialed, hoping he hadn't screwed up too badly.

"Danny, this is Ben. Listen, I need to ask you a lawyer question."

"Shoot."

"It's about sexual harassment laws."

"Did you get yourself in trouble?" Danny asked quietly.

"God, I hope not. I don't think so. It's Dad's company, not mine. Last thing I want is to mess it up."

"Um, this a consensual situation?"

Now that was the million-dollar question. He had no idea. Ben told Danny what had happened and then sighed as he wrapped up the sorry tale. "Could I get her to sign a waiver or something?" he asked, and immediately thought of her nonexistent sense of humor, and figured it'd be easier to herd cats than get a signature from her, but he'd do whatever he had to.

"A waiver? Ben, relax. You're fine. If she starts making noises, call me back. But I don't see a case there."

Ben let out a long sigh of relief. "Thanks."

"Don't mention it. Haven't seen you since you got back in town. What are you up for next?"

"Cowboy."

"Rodeo? Whoa, dogies."

"Nope. Just roping and stuff."

"Still, pretty cool. Hey, what are you doing tomorrow? The guys are going to OutdoorLand to check out their hiking gear. Got a big trip planned in a couple of weeks. You gotta come."

Ben leaned back in his chair and put his feet up on the desk. Hiking, now that he could handle. "Sounds like fun."

"See you on Saturday," Danny said, and then hung up.

One bullet dodged.

Ben put down the phone and swiveled his chair to face the window. What was he doing here? Downtown Dallas. Rain. Buildings everywhere.

Being a businessman really was the pits so far. Out on the range, there was only the wind and the sky. And the last thing a cowboy had to worry about was sexual harassment.

Damn.

4

Two hours later Ben was driving in the downpour, with squeaking windshield wipers and all. Miss Hilary Sinclair had disappeared from MacAllister Beds, last seen exiting to the parking lot, leaving one rumpled bedsheet behind her. He peered through the rain, scanning the painted numbers on the sidewalk.

Her personnel file listed her address as just south of the river in Kessler Park, a small community full of young families that were remodeling the older homes. Finally he found what he was looking for, although when he looked carefully, he wondered if he'd made a mistake.

The grass was knee-high and in sore need of weeding. Of the three concrete steps that led to the front door, two were cracked, and one was missing. The house was kind of cute, with an A-line roof and the dark red bricks so popular long ago. But still...

Ben knew Miss Sinclair was a little messy, but this seemed extreme. He pulled up the collar of his overcoat and then made his way to the front door.

He nearly laughed at the little horseshoe that was hanging over the door knocker. Jeez, this house needed more than a horseshoe, but he didn't think Miss Sinclair would take kindly to having him laugh at her house. He put on his best poker face and rang the bell.

"Hello?"

"Miss Sinclair, it's Ben MacAllister."

She cracked her door open and peered at him suspiciously. "Mr. MacAllister, what are you doing here?"

"Could I come in?"

For a moment he thought she would refuse, not that he could blame her, but then the door swung open. She was dressed in an old terry-cloth robe, and her nose looked red and irritated.

Had she been crying? He started to touch her, and realized that's what had gotten him in trouble in the first place.

"Are you all right?"

"Why are you here?" she asked, her voice raspy, and he realized she was sick. He felt the first stirrings of what he hoped was sympathy. It was a depraved man who felt desire for a woman who looked to be running 103° temperature. He cleared his throat. "I came to apologize."

Hilary didn't say a word, but when she walked inside, he assumed it was an invitation to follow.

And then stopped.

It was a nightmare of Bob Villa proportions.

A truss had sheared through the side wall and was embedded like a pickax. Rain was pouring into a small bucket that looked about to overflow. There was a ladder and tools set up, a home improvement book lay open on the top step of the ladder. Gently, he shut the front door, afraid to be the cause of any more new disasters.

She looked up at him defiantly, waiting for a wiseass remark.

"You've got a leak," he said, trying for honesty.

She sneezed. "Magnificent deduction. I can see why you're in charge in security."

If she thought she'd get a rise out of him, she was mistaken. He wasn't up to kicking puppies or insulting sickly women with leaking roofs. "I'm sorry," he repeated, apologizing more for her roof than anything else.

She waved a hand and then eased herself into a chair. "Forget about it. I would offer you a seat, but most of them are soaked."

"Is that why you've been sleeping in the research center?"

Hilary winced but didn't deny it. "Sorry. You won't say anything, will you? I just need to get this fixed."

Ben shook his head and then took a good look around. Something definitely akin to sympathy tugged at him.

Altruism wasn't one of Ben's finer qualities, but suddenly he realized he wanted to help. Here was someone who needed him. "Want a hand?" he asked, hoping she'd say yes.

"Know a roofer?"

He blew out a breath. "I could fix it for you."

"And what would you want in return?"

She didn't make altruism easy, but he wasn't going to give up. "Is it just me, or do you not trust anyone?"

She crossed her arms over her chest and stared up at him. "Just the ones who've had their hands on my breasts."

Automatically his fingers flexed in memory, but he held on tightly to thoughts of altruism. "Let's not go there right now. It's raining in your living room. I can fix it for you. No favors necessary."

Her green eyes looked a little bleary, but they still held suspicion. "Swear?"

"Swear."

For a moment he thought she was going to say no, but finally she nodded agreement. "All right. How are you going to fix it?"

"We'll put up some plastic sheeting first, and that'll dry things off some. After that, a couple of two-by-fours, and you'll be in business temporarily. It's nothing more than a patch, but it'll hold for a while."

Hilary wiped her eyes with a tissue. "You're all right."

"Got any chicken soup?"

"Hungry?"

"No, but you look like you could use some. I could go to the store if your cupboard is bare." She looked like a woman with bare cupboards.

"You trying to get on my good side?"

"Do you have a good side, Miss Sinclair?"

Hilary smiled, a little wobbly, but bright enough to stop the rain. "If you're not careful, Mr. MacAllister, I'm going to change my opinion of you."

Quickly Ben climbed up the ladder, suddenly needing to study the hole in her ceiling.

On a more rational day, it would have been easy to stay away from Hilary Sinclair. She was prickly and arrogant and obviously didn't like him. But for the past few months, he'd felt decidedly irrational. Ben stole a quick look down, and caught her smile.

Whoa. Definitely irrational.

HILARY SAT CURLED UP on the corner chair, sipping hot tea and watching as Ben worked on her ceiling. The cold medicine she'd taken was starting to make her woozy, but she didn't want to sleep, she just wanted to sit here and watch him in action. He didn't say much, which surprised her. She had figured the Ben MacAllisters of the world didn't understand the value of silence.

She knew about those charming types who always had a joke or an insincere compliment. The guys that liked to regale the world with the tales of their exploits.

Before today she would have bet her Visa bill that Ben was one of them.

But she was wrong about him.

Being wrong never sat well with Hilary, and eventually it bugged her so much that she turned on the stereo, just to fill the silence that was far too comforting. At six o'clock, the calm, melodious tones of Dr. Tracy filled the house.

"Do you mind listening to her?" she asked, liking the way he moved as he worked. His shirt hung loose on his frame, and she could see the strong lines of his arms and back as he lifted the boards into place.

Ben picked up a nail and began to hammer. "Dr. Tracy? She's a little opinionated, don't you think?"

"Sometimes, but I don't think it hurts to take a stand on things."

"No, I guess not," he said, a smile playing around his mouth.

He was humoring her. Hilary didn't take humoring lightly. "I bet you think she's too old-fashioned," she shot back.

"I didn't say that."

"You didn't have to."

"She's my sister-in-law."

"No kidding? That's so amazing."

Ben shrugged. "I'm surprised Allen didn't tell you the first day you walked in the door. That's what he does to just about everyone else. He's real proud of her. Thinks she knows everything."

"Because she does. You should try doing her job sometime," Hilary snapped. Guys like him thought everything was so easy. Life was just one big piece of chocolate cake. Dr. Tracy knew better.

Their eyes met, hers daring, his amused. "Okay, we'll play advice counselor. Turn up the volume."

Hilary adjusted the knob and they both listened to the female caller's voice.

"Dr. Tracy, I'm eighteen, and I'm in love with a great guy. We've only known each other for about six months, but I can tell that he's the one. We've been talking about marriage, but I know my parents won't approve. What should I do?"

Hilary muted the radio and shot a curious look at Ben. "So, what is your advice, Dr. MacAllister?"

He put down the hammer and leaned on the top step of the ladder. "Elope. Skip the confrontation with the parents and just go for it. *Et tu*, Dr. Sinclair?"

Just as she had suspected. Fly-by-night. Entirely irresponsible. She took a sip of tea, mulling over her response. "What about college? What about learning what this guy is about? What if he's a deadbeat?"

Ben lifted another board and she got a little dry in the mouth in the presence of such amazing biceps.

She nearly missed his response. "What about love?" he asked.

At that exact moment in the world, she was sure that some little porker had just sprung wings. "You're a romantic."

"No, just practical."

"How so?"

"If things don't work out, a divorce, no harm, no foul."

Trust a man to be so slapdash about marriage. Mark hadn't been slapdash. "They should wait. Take their time. Eighteen is too young to get married, and divorce is not an option."

He shot her a curious look. "Catholic, Miss Sinclair?"

Hilary raised her chin. "No, I just have high standards." Too late. She realized that she might have put her foot in it. "Have you been married before, Mr. MacAllister?"

"Nope."

"So you have loads of experience to draw on?"

"Have you been married before, Miss Sinclair?"

"No."

"What about Mark?"

Instantly Hilary was back in Atlanta, back in the condo, eating Thursday-night lasagna and playing poker. Mark couldn't stand to lose, so she would always let him win. In seven years, he never caught on. He just thought she was a crappy player. She drew up her knees tightly, reluctant to talk to Ben about Mark. She'd already mistaken him for Mark once and look where that got her. "You almost done up there?"

Ben picked up the hammer once more and began pounding. "Yeah. Just a few minutes."

They were as different as two men could be. Mark had dark hair, cut in a short, practical manner. Ben had light brown hair that never seemed to stay in place. Mark was steady and reliable. But Ben MacAllister was a 24/7 candy store that believed in free samples. The man coasted on a wink and a smile.

Yet there was Mr. Unreliable, stuck on a ladder fixing her ceiling.

How did that work? Hilary shook her head, feeling too tired to contemplate the possibility of being wrong twice in one evening.

She leaned her head back against the soft cushions of her chair and listened as Dr. Tracy dispatched words of wisdom—agreeing with Hilary, of course—and gloried in the amazing power of Mr. Unreliable's biceps.

IT WAS ALMOST TEN o'clock before her roof was somewhat restored. The boards looked pretty unsightly, unfinished pine over mangled Sheetrock, but it was a small price to pay now that it no longer rained in her house. If it really got to her, she supposed she could paint it a fashionable shade of purple. Ben finished packing up her tools and collapsed on her couch.

"Why don't you get some sleep?" he said, pushing wayward hair out of his eyes. "You look wiped." Actually, she thought he was being kind. She felt miserable, but she couldn't quite force herself to stop watching him. It was like staring after a car wreck. You hate yourself for doing it, but you can't bring yourself to avoid it, either.

"You're sitting on my bed."

It was as if she'd told him he was sitting on nitro. He jumped up, and then took a good look around the place. She was too drained to be embarrassed, but her toes curled anyway. She'd never been an incredibly material person, but she did have some pride.

"You don't own anything, do you?" he asked, now leaning against the back of the couch, his hands jammed in his pockets. She watched her pride flutter out the window.

"I manage," she said, tossing her head in a very Mae manner.

"Yeah," he answered, a wealth of disbelief in the word, the Mae gesture completely wasted.

It was an odd moment. She knew he should leave, and he knew he should leave as well. Yet, both of them continued talking, trading barbs, as if it was the most natural thing in the world. An insidious memory crept into her mind, the feel of his mouth at her breast. Suddenly the soft material of her robe became unbearable.

He seemed to feel the tension as well. "Stay at home tomorrow. Get well." He picked up his overcoat and started to the door.

"I have a conference call scheduled in the morning," she said, willing him to stay.

"I can get Helga to reschedule it for you," he answered, shrugging into the coat.

"No. I want to renegotiate the rate we're getting for cotton batting, and I've finally gotten on the calendar with a VP at Masters Bonded Fibers."

"Then I'll take the call for you."

He sounded serious. Even in the drug-induced haze

of her brain, she recognized the sincerity in his voice. Curious, she studied him, searching for the punch line. But there didn't seem to be one. "No offense, but I can handle it."

His face cleared, all sincerity gone. Instead, he assumed the vacant look that he seemed to have perfected and shook a warning finger at her. "Fine. Take the call, be stubborn, but if the entire company comes down with the flu, I'm holding you personally responsible."

"I don't have the flu," she said, mainly because she felt like crap and didn't like listening to lectures.

Ben stopped in the doorway, then swore softly and turned around. "You do have blankets, don't you?"

"There are a couple in the back room."

"Go lie down then," he said, with a gesture at the couch.

While he retrieved the bed linens, Hilary sank gratefully onto the long, leather couch. Her bones felt as if they were made of water, and as she lay down, she sighed in relief.

A warm blanket covered her, her herbal pillow placed under her head. She closed her eyes, comfortable for the first time in days.

For a moment he stroked her hair with a gentle hand. "Good night, Hilary Sinclair."

"Good night, Ben MacAllister."

There was a click as he flipped off the lights, and the

room was shrouded in the night, the rain no longer a miserable thing, now it seemed more like a friend.

He walked toward the door, and she lifted her head up, watching his silhouette in the darkness. "Ben?"

At her voice, he stopped, and she stared after him. Another time she might have asked him to stay, but it wouldn't be this night. He wasn't the right man, so "Thank you" was what she ended up saying.

"Don't mention it," he replied, and left.

Once more Hilary was all alone. After she heard the whir of his engine, and she was sure he was gone, she crept back into her bedroom and took Benjamin Franklin from his box.

She crawled back under the blankets, Benjamin securely at her side.

THE NEXT MORNING, Ben had scavenged all the documentation he could on MacAllister Beds. The *Hacking Exposed* book was stowed far back in his desk drawer. He had bigger plans, now, not that they were going so well. He could do more than security. In only one week he'd gotten a rudimentary understanding of mattress design, next up was finance. He was slugging through the quarterly statement when Hilary walked into his office.

Today she didn't wear her usual skirt and hose; instead, she was dressed in jeans and a T-shirt. And he would have been remiss not to notice the two coffee blotches on the T-shirt front and center. She could look like death warmed over, but God forbid, apparently didn't skimp on the coffee.

Stubborn woman. "I thought I told you to stay home," he said, trying for a tone of authority.

Rather than answer him, she went to his white board and wrote, *I can't talk.*

Ben stalked over to the white board and wrote back. *Go home.*

I have the call, she wrote.

He put down his marker. "Go home. I'll reschedule it for you."

Hilary stared at him, murder in her eyes, and shook her head.

Stubborn, he scrawled, underlining it heavily.

I need your help.

Ben stared at the lopsided words that she had scribbled and smiled. How had she managed in Atlanta?

Oh yeah—Mark. That's how she had done it. Still he couldn't help the leap in his voice, couldn't stop the simple hope. "What do you want?"

Take the call on the speakerphone. I can write what you need to say.

He rocked back on his heels, frustrated that she had so little trust in him. "Okay, but at least tell me what you want to do, so I'm not blindsided by anything."

She studied him, looking ready for battle, but apparently she saw the futility in a white-board debate. She nodded and picked up the marker. *Here's what we need to do.*

It took about an hour and a half, but by the time she was done, Ben was feeling pretty good. She simply wanted to renegotiate the rates and volumes for the cotton fiber. He could do that, and he even had a few more ideas, but he kept those to himself.

At noon, she was situated in his office and he dialed out.

"John Spears speaking."

"John, this is Ben MacAllister from MacAllister Beds."

"Oh, hello Mr. MacAllister. I had thought we were scheduled with Ms. Sinclair, but of course we're always happy to talk with the owner."

Click...click...click. Ben watched as Hilary repeatedly capped and uncapped the marker. Finally she wrote. *Owner, schmowner.*

Ben was actually starting to enjoy her loss of voice. Just to tick her off, he smiled broadly and resumed his conversation.

"Ah, yes. Now what we're trying to do is—"

Furiously she scribbled on the board and Ben repeated what she wrote. "...evaluate the value proposition with Masters, and to be honest, we're not sure we're there yet." Getting a little confident, he started to put in things on his own. "In these times, we just need to stay aware of the market and what's driving it. Customer commitment, that's what makes MacAllister Beds, and primary among those commitments is price."

Hilary rolled her eyes. He winked back at her.

"Well, of course, aren't we all? But we're already giving you the best numbers we can."

Hilary scribbled and Ben read. "We've found some more competitive pricing from Midwest Cotton and before we make any changes, we wanted to give Masters an opportunity to match the quotes."

There was some hemming and hawing on the line. "Well, of course, our quality can't be beat. You don't want to put shoddy fiber into your mattresses."

Again Hilary picked up her pen and wrote. *Midwest was rated number one by The National Institute of Fiber. Can't argue with that. I believe Masters was number five.*

Ben looked at Hilary with appreciation. *Good job,* he mouthed, and then read the information to Spears.

"Perhaps we can do something about it," the man answered.

Hilary folded her arms across her chest and smiled, completely confident in her abilities. For the first time in his short time at MacAllister Beds, Ben felt the thrill of the chase. "And while you're at it, John, maybe you can re-evaluate those contracts for the organic cotton for our hypoallergenic line. Just due diligence after all." Hilary's eyes widened and she shook her head. Ben ignored her.

"We'll do that, Mr. MacAllister. I'll be back in touch on Monday with a new quote."

"For both products?"

"For both products. Always a pleasure, Mr. Mac-Allister."

"The pleasure is all mine, Mr. Spears. All mine."

He hung up the phone, leaned back in his chair and locked his hands behind his head. Not even lunchtime and already they'd renegotiated the pricing structure with one of their main suppliers.

Hilary didn't look happy, though. She was watching him warily, as if he'd suddenly turned into the enemy.

"What?" he said, wishing he didn't sound so defensive.

She shook her head and pointed to her throat.

"Want to have lunch? Chicken soup? I'll buy."

For a moment she chewed on her lip, indecision wavering in her eyes. Eventually she shook her head and went to the white board. *I'm going home.*

Surely that wasn't disappointment that stuck in his throat. Couldn't be. "Smart move. Do you need anything?"

Again with the head shake. She looked as if she could use a few days of recuperation. There were dark circles under her eyes and she had worn her hair pulled back in a ponytail. No humidity hair today.

She turned to go, and before he knew what he was doing, he had moved around his desk. He hadn't meant to touch her, but there was his hand on her arm. He had known that would be a bad idea, but he needed to touch her, and Ben had never been a master of self-control.

Hilary stopped and stared at his hand. She didn't move away, just stood, frozen.

"You'll tell me if you have any more problems, won't you?" he asked.

Hilary looked up at him, green eyes wide and unblinking. Slowly she nodded.

He had moved one step closer, when Helga walked in the door.

Hilary turned and ran from the room.

"Yes?" Ben managed to ask.

"You wanted to see the access logs for the research center?" She piled a stack of papers on his desk. "There you are."

"Thank you, Helga," he said. "I'll get right on it. Can you close the door behind you?"

The efficient dragon lady closed the door and left the room, and Ben leafed through the papers. Not long after, he abandoned the reports. He couldn't concentrate, so he clicked on his solitaire icon and began to play. He wondered if she was any good at games. She certainly was good at the mattress biz. He could be that good with the proper guidance.

Too bad his dad didn't seem interested in providing that guidance. But Hilary could. Maybe she could teach him? After all, they were a pretty good team. He had the charm and the wits, she had the brains and the background. Would she do it, though?

Probably not, unless he could find a way to twist her

arm. He drummed his fingers on his desk, while turning over the possibilities in his mind.

"ARE MY CHESS TROPHIES still up here, Mom?" Allen's voice drifted down from the attic. Ben looked around the downstairs of what had been his family home. There were boxes everywhere, newspapers scrunched into balls of packing material, and thirty-two-year-old dust mites floating in the air. In the middle of all the chaos stood his mother, completely at peace.

Mary Lynn MacAllister smiled, and yelled up the staircase. "Yes, Allen. Give me a minute and I'll be right up. It's just behind your old stereo system."

His brother's answer came from above. "You still have that? That's great!"

Ben shook his head helplessly, his family rummaging through their old house like a band of marauding warriors, pillaging every nook and cranny. Jealously he guarded his four boxes, four boxes which contained his life from birth to the present day.

Four little boxes. Soccer trophies, math certificates, the ribbon from his piano lessons, and assorted class pictures from elementary school, junior high, high school and college. Somewhere deep in the bowels of that box was a picture of him still in braces escorting Sheila Answorthy to the prom. He shuddered every time he remembered that photograph. Yeesh.

His mother tapped him on the shoulder, startling

him. "Ben, you going to stand there like a zombie or are you going to order lunch?"

Lunch. It sounded so mundane, so common-place. Was he the only one who saw the irony? Probably.

He kept his mouth shut and dialed. Hunger was not the need that rolled in his stomach, but everyone else wanted pepperoni and onion, and who was he to argue?

He was just hanging up the phone when his dad bounded down the wooden stairs, face flushed with excitement. "Have you seen my new toy?" Martin held out a color brochure, the Winnebago Vista. Galley, bedroom, and satellite TV.

Ben forced a smile. "Gee, Dad, looks great. Gonna go out and see the U.S.A.?"

"I thought so. Finally have a chance to look out over the Grand Canyon. Didn't you go camping there when you were in high school? What'd you think?"

"It's big."

His dad spread his arms wide, then beat his chest. "Fresh air. That's what I need. You always had the right idea. Should have listened to you earlier. What's your next adventure, Ben?"

"Cowboy," he answered, wishing he could say something more ambitious, more intelligent—like senator.

"Maybe we could go together? Father and son, riding the range. Bet that'll stir some blood."

"Yeah, Dad, it sure will." Ben took a moment to shove his boxes behind him, out of his father's reach.

"How're you liking the job, Ben? Too tame for you, huh? Figured you were going to get tired of it."

Ben laughed, remembering how long he had debated his decision to take the job at MacAllister Beds. "Actually, it's not as bad as I expected."

Martin stuck his hands in his pockets, keys jingling. "Oh, ho! High praise, indeed." His father leaned against the newel and Ben remembered sliding down the stairwell when he was seven, his father there to catch him.

"Dad, did you ever consider moving the production facilities to Mexico? Seems like we're being charged an arm and a leg from Pickens."

"You going to talk shop with me today of all days? Talk to Allen. If anyone is interested, it'll be him."

Maybe he should drop the whole idea? Concentrate on the hiking trip. He wasn't needed here. "Sure, Dad," he said.

His mother's voice came from upstairs. "Ben, can you come pick up this box of books? It's yours, I'm sure of it."

Eager to escape his father, Ben took the stairs two at a time and found his mother sitting on the floor of what had been his room, surrounded by copies of *The Hardy Boys* and *Encyclopedia Brown*.

"What would you like to do with this?"

On top of the books sat his old hacky sack. He

scooped it up and tossed it high into the air. "I'll take it all home with me. Thanks for keeping this stuff."

His mother picked up a bundle of newspapers and walked to the corner where her curio cabinets stood. "Are you all right, Benjamin?"

Nothing got by his mom. Not playing hooky from school, not cheating on an algebra test, not wondering what he was going to count on anymore. "Of course. I'm more worried about you."

"Oh, pshaw. Don't you worry about me, none. The new apartment has been fun, and I don't miss the dust in this old place one bit. The apartment's temporary, though. I've got my eye on the new seniors' development north of town. Margaret Toddleston bought a house over there last year and has been after me to move to the neighborhood."

Visions of shuffleboard filled his head and he shook that nightmare away. "A seniors' development? Mom, you're too young for that."

"You don't understand, Ben. I do want to kick up my heels a bit, but I'm not ready to go traipsing around the country like your father. You and he are just alike. I need my roots. I'm looking forward to it." She laughed aloud, blue eyes twinkling. "You know what?"

"What?"

"They have dance lessons twice a week. Ballroom, country and western, and even salsa dancing. Your father hated to dance. I should've known that was a sign."

Ben took the box of books and shoved it behind him. "You don't have to get divorced just because you want to take dancing lessons."

His mother smiled, gently, as she had when he was a kid. "Ben, your father is a wonderful man, and I will miss him desperately, but I've always known something was absent from our marriage. Something that should have been there. We both knew it, we're just now being honest."

He looked around the room. Four walls and a wooden floor. This had been his room at one time, but now it was nothing more than a showcase for his mom's collectibles—little statues of flowers and birds, and dancing figurines. "But why now? Surely you're happier together than apart, even with something missing. It's not like you and Dad hate each other."

His mother wrapped a porcelain ballerina in newsprint and packed it away. "I'll never hate your father. He gave you and Allen to me, and that's something I will always be grateful for. I just think it's time for me to be out on my own. What if there's somebody special out there? Don't I deserve that?"

"Of course you do, Mom." A dangerous thought occurred, and he shot her a suspicious look. "You haven't already found somebody, have you? Is that what this is about?"

His mother laughed and plucked a dainty cardinal from the shelf. "No, Ben. But I want to. Your father was never my true love, and it's time for me to find the man who is. I want romance, Ben. Passion."

"I don't think passion can replace companionship and friendship. Passion doesn't last, Mom."

"And now we have two relationship experts in the family?" she asked, lifting a brow.

Ben stuffed his hands in his pockets. "Okay, point made. I've said my piece. If you need anything, let me know."

"I don't know what I need, Ben, but at least I now have a chance of finding out." The doorbell rang and his mother walked downstairs, wiping her hands on her apron. "That's the pizza. Let's go eat."

Ben followed behind, carrying his last box of treasures. It looked as though he was going to have to find a new life, because his old one was disappearing one box at a time.

THE ENTIRE MACALLISTER CLAN was gathered around the kitchen table, cleaning out a pizza box in the same brutally efficient manner as the house.

After four hours of packing, everyone looked rumpled and in desperate need of a shower. Only Tracy looked well pressed, her white slacks immaculate. Of course, Tracy prided herself on her organizational abilities, not on her willingness to pitch in and help.

But Allen seemed to love her and as far as Ben knew, they weren't getting divorced.

Ben was finishing his last piece of pizza when his brother spoke up. "What do you think of Hilary, Ben?"

Ben looked up in midchew.

Tracy adjusted her tortoiseshell glasses and stared with interest. "Who's Hilary?"

"She works at the company." Ben dodged his brother's look. "She's okay."

His father took the last piece from the box. "More than okay. Never met a woman who understood mattresses so well. Too bad about her packaging, though."

His mom picked up their plates and took them over to the sink. "What do you mean?"

"You know, women are either blessed with brains or beauty. God knows better than to give them both. Hilary got overcompensated in the brains department. Lucky for me."

"Martin MacAllister, that is the most sexist remark I've ever heard you say."

"Get used to 'em, Mary Lynn. I'm a free man."

"I don't think there's anything wrong with her packaging," said Ben, surprising himself.

"Me, neither," Allen agreed.

His wife shot him a what-does-that-mean? look and he recanted. "Okay, she's not like a supermodel or anything, she's just...average."

Mary Lynn turned on the water and began to load the dishes in the dishwasher. "She's the girl you hired from Atlanta, Martin? She's single, isn't she? Maybe she and I should go out together."

"I'd like to meet her. Maybe the three of us can go for dinner and a movie," Tracy added, obviously not completely trusting Allen's judgment.

Mary Lynn bobbed her head. "Perfect. I'll call her and we can show her the town."

Ben took a swig of cola and worked to keep his mouth shut. Hilary wasn't average. Okay, maybe her nose was a little large, and maybe her hair wasn't the stuff of shampoo commercials, but her eyes could trap you if your weren't careful, she had a nice smile, and well, to be honest, he'd never seen a rack that was so perfectly made. If that made him a sexist, just like his dad, so be it.

Tracy picked up her glass and dinged her fork against the side of it. "Well, now that that's all settled...everyone, we have an announcement."

Babies. Good God, now they were done for. Ben waited for the news that Allen had managed to procreate.

Tracy continued. "As you know, *The Dr. Tracy Hour* has been doing very well in the Dallas radio market and an L.A. radio station is very excited about my work. They've picked up the show and are expanding it to three hours."

Mary Lynn gave Tracy a warm hug. "Oh, you're going to be syndicated!"

Tracy drew back, adjusting her glasses. "Well, not exactly. It will be broadcast from L.A., but we're hoping for syndication soon."

"We're moving to L.A.!" Allen said, unable to keep quiet any longer.

Ben cut to the chase. "And who's going to take over for you at MacAllister Beds?"

Ben's father cleared his throat and waited until he had all eyes. "Allen came to me a couple of weeks ago and told me about the situation. Got me thinking. I think it's time to sell the company. Life's too short to just spend the whole time doing work, work, work."

Ben pushed his glass away and stared at his father. This was too much. "Sell?"

"Yup. I think it's time to hang up my boots and, with Allen leaving, it seems the perfect solution." He smiled, pleased with himself.

"And that's it? You want to sell it, so, poof—it's gone?"

Martin frowned, a blank expression on his face, as if there were no other alternatives. "Well, yes."

Ben slammed his hand on the table, and even Tracy jumped. "Has everyone gone mad? First the divorce, then selling the house, now Allen is moving to L.A., and the only thing you can think of is to sell the business? If y'all will excuse me, I've got to go buy some hiking gear."

The air seemed to choke him. Thick and suffocating. He had thought someone would notice. Someone would realize that this time Ben was here to stay. He'd come back home to help, but no one seemed to *need* him. No one, that is, except for Hilary.

Ben was nearly to the front door when he turned around to glare at his father. "You need new glasses, Dad, the old ones aren't working anymore, because Hilary's packaging is just fine."

SATURDAY AFTERNOON BROUGHT an eclectic crowd to OutdoorLand. There were the Birkenstock shoppers, serious and thoughtful, who tried on shoes and tromped around the store with Mount Everest aspirations. It was the kind of place that lent itself to big dreams.

Last-minute cyclists came dressed in bike shorts and jerseys to pick up that extra inner tube for road emergencies. Families showed up with kids, who climbed in and out of the tents in a sophisticated game of hide-and-seek, squealing when their parents caught them.

And then there was the *wall*.

Ben had been fourteen the first time his father had taken him to the store. That day he'd asked permission to climb.

"You can't make it to the top, Ben," his father had said. "Come on, let's go look at a bicycle for you."

But Ben came back the next day—sneaked out of the house riding his brand-new bicycle—and conquered the wall. It was a snap. His dad had never known.

Now the wall didn't look quite so formidable. The challenge was gone.

"Ben!"

He turned at the sound of his name, and saw Jason

waving at him from behind an overturned kayak. Danny, Robert and Steven milled about behind him, apparently comparing notes on the durability of Polartec outerwear while they waited for Ben to make his way over.

In high school, they were five together. Five hundred-percent-guaranteed hell-raisers. As teenagers, they had believed in the intoxicating power of their own immortality. No feat too small, no dare too dangerous.

First to shake his hand was Danny. He was always in the lead. Magna cum laude, S.M.U. School of Law. And then there was Jason who had been the first one to fall asleep during Mr. Minter's calculus class. Now he taught eleventh grade math in South Dallas.

Robert was the criminal of the group. Shoplifting, hot-wiring, he was the one who always "knew things." It was no surprise that he was now a Dallas cop, married to his high school sweetheart, and expecting their third child.

And bringing up the rear stood Steven, nondescript, fade-into-the-background Steven, who had just started his own engineering firm.

"Hey, glad to see you back!" Jason slapped him on the back, still wearing the same old monogrammed baseball cap. Tall and lanky, he carried the nickname Beanpole proudly. He still wore a perpetual grin, but the look in his eyes had changed. Now it was shrewder, wiser. Jason wasn't a clown anymore.

"How long you here for this time?" asked Robert, sporting a spare tire around his middle these days. There were purple pen marks on the shoulder of his white sports shirt, and new lines around his eyes. Ben figured the lines were from lack of sleep, but he also recognized them as lines of laughter.

"I think I'll be here for a while," Ben answered, moving out of the path of an oncoming roller-blader.

Jason shook his head. "Yowza, sounds permanent."

"No more permanent than usual." Tired of trying to see over Jason, Ben pulled Steve forward. "How you doing?"

Steve had changed as well. He was taller, broader, a lot more confident than the boy who had had two dates in high school.

He stuck out his hand for the obligatory male handshake. Automatically Ben responded. All his friends were different now. Was he different, too?

It was like a bad *Twilight Zone* episode. He had changed, but he wasn't sure how.

Well, today he wouldn't care.

Ben eyed his friends, eyed the wall.

"Last one to the top buys the beer," he said, with a two-foot head start, and then he began to climb for real.

Danny caught up fast. "You always were a cheat, MacAllister."

But Ben had always been quick, too. He stretched upward, reaching for a handhold and then shot forward. "You should have learned by now."

Before it had even started, it was over. Ben won.

Robert stayed at the bottom and just laughed at them all. "Beer's on Jason."

From high atop the wall, Jason used his index finger to flash Robert the universal sign of peace and goodwill. "Just cause you don't play, doesn't mean you don't pay."

Robert pulled on his cop face. "I could have you arrested for that, son."

There were Robert and Jason, cutting up like usual. Maybe things hadn't changed all that much.

Ben had climbed back down to the ground and jammed his hands in his pockets. He let the filter of conversation wash over him.

Slowly, they walked the store, and Ben felt trapped in the past.

By the canoes, he told his best jokes. When they wandered through the bicycles, Ben dazzled them with tales of his conquests.

Except for Hilary. To be fair, Hilary was not a woman that a man conquered, she was a woman a man survived. If he was lucky. If Danny noticed the omission, he didn't bring it up. There was an advantage to sharing secrets with a lawyer.

When they passed by the snow skis, Ben tossed out the latest news on baseball's opening day, but by the time they were in the hiking section, he had run out of things to say.

Thankfully, Steven filled the silence before anyone noticed. "How was Vegas?"

Vegas. Now there was a memory he could hold on to. The lights, the noise, the chaos. Heaven. "I ended up ahead, but not by much."

Danny looked at Ben over the display of trail maps. "Who ended up winning the poker tournament?"

"Some old geezer from Philly. He'd been playing all his life. A rookie like me didn't stand a chance."

"Ah, but you got to do it," said Robert, who hadn't been outside the state of Texas since he'd visited Arkansas in the second grade.

Ben picked up a pair of boots from the display and examined the outer soles. The traction would be good on these things, especially in the rain. "I'm trying my hand at the executive lifestyle now," Ben said, running a finger over the leather uppers.

There was much laughter because everybody knew that Ben wasn't executive material.

"It's the girl, isn't it?" Danny asked, the only one who suspected it wasn't meant to be a joke.

"No," Ben answered quietly. He hadn't told anyone about the divorce. How did you bring that up? How did you say your parents are splitting up? You didn't. "Maybe," he equivocated. It was easier.

Jason twisted his cap on his head. "So when are we going to meet her, old man?"

"Never." God, they would never understand Hilary.

"Hey, Robert, you been practicing your diaper-changing skills?"

And the conversation was effectively diverted to safer subjects.

Eventually, all the purchases were made and they migrated to the parking lot. Ben had settled on a new pair of boots that he could test out on the trip. "So, where we headed on this journey?"

Robert hoisted his bags into a red minivan that was coated with crackers and fries. "Lake Mineral Wells. Not too far." He slammed the rear door shut and then leaned against it.

"Y'all going to climb?"

Jason opened the door to his car, an old white Dodge. Four cylinders. A far cry from the Trans-Am he drove in high school. "Do fish swim? You in?"

"Hell, yes."

After Jason, Steven and Robert had left, Danny walked Ben to his truck. The red Ford stood waiting, beat up from years of wear, but still with a big enough bed for whatever he decided to bring home.

"Women are invited—nay, my friend—they are expected," Danny said while Ben took out his keys.

"Is this a setup?"

"Would we do that?"

"Yes," Ben answered, relieved to have the decision off his conscience. Wasn't this what he wanted? Hadn't he been searching for a way to get her in his bed?

Maybe it wasn't something that he'd been ready to admit. Hilary was an anomaly.

But he wanted her badly, just the same.

"Tell you what. If you want to be the only man who cannot provide himself with feminine companionship for two measly days, then go right ahead. Be your own man. And we will have you pegged for the loser that you are. But—" Danny held up a finger "—if you show up, woman in tow, I will personally provide you with free legal advice for the rest of your natural-born life."

"Now that's a proposition worth—" Ben scratched his chin "—zero."

Danny held up his hands, scale-of-justice style. "Worthy man, worthless man. Your choice."

Which left him with no choice at all. "I'll be there."

"Alone?"

Ben just laughed. Confident, cocky, but completely clueless as to how he could get Hilary to agree.

SATURDAY NIGHTS in Atlanta had never been this boring, Hilary thought to herself, staring at the laptop screen in front of her and nibbling on her pencil. Oh, whine, whine, whine. At least the plans for the conference were coming along nicely. Marketing wasn't her normal forte, but with the current director of marketing laid up with a broken leg, Hilary was more than happy to pitch in and help. And after all, lining up interviews wasn't a tough job. The list of media contacts had some familiar names and some new ones. When it came to the mattress biz, the world was a small place.

She liked the busywork. It gave her a chance to forget about the heartache she had left behind in Georgia.

Pushing that depressing thought away, Hilary picked up the phone to call Julie Daly from *SleepTimes* magazine and then realized she'd only get Julie's voice mail. Groaning in frustration, she went back to the laptop. Work was good, work was good, work was good. She was not going bonkers.

At seven o'clock, she padded into the kitchen for her usual Saturday night menu. Omelettes. Mark had liked ham, cheese, peppers and onions, lightly browned, not runny. Tonight she'd rebel and leave off the peppers. A small step, but one in the right direction.

Supper was soon ready and so she turned on the radio for some music to eat by. No music tonight though and no Dr. Tracy. Instead the sounds of spring baseball filled the room. Mark had loved baseball. Hilary had liked the uniforms. Quickly, she turned it off, and sat on the couch, prepared to eat her pepperless omelette.

Just as she took the first bite, the doorbell rang. Company? She put the plate aside and checked the peephole.

Ben MacAllister. Dapper, dashing and daunting. Nervously she scrunched her toes, and took in her own sweats and T-shirt.

Crap.

5

THE FIRST THING Hilary noticed was his smile. Every girl knows the smile of a man who plans on getting lucky. Seen at bars around the world at closing time, and most recently here standing on her doorstep.

Every survival instinct told her to slam the door in his face.

She invited him in.

Loser.

And then she noticed the bottle of wine he carried. *Beware the Trojan horse.* Probably carried Trojans in his back pocket, too. "It's very late."

"I was in the neighborhood."

"I see," she said dryly, wishing she could run to the bathroom and put on makeup.

"Your light was on."

She looked pointedly at the forty-watt light emanating from her lonely floor lamp. "Yes, it is."

He handed her the bottle. "I brought you some wine."

She pointed to her glass on the coffee table. "I already have some, thanks."

"You're not going to make this easy, are you?" he said, disappointment in his eyes.

The air grew tight and still. At that moment Hilary wished she were the sort of woman who could just say yes. Mae would say yes.

"I think you've got me confused with someone else," she said, wishing her heart wasn't so bruised.

"Why?" he asked, still smiling.

And how was she supposed to answer that one? "Because," she said, and left it at that.

She stood, hands crossed across her chest, loins girded.

Blissfully unaware of her inner turmoil, he sat down on the couch and made himself comfortable.

"Hilary, come on. You're an adult, I'm an adult..." He held out a hand to her.

There, on her living room couch, sat the devil. His hair just waiting for her touch, eyes full of sin, and like gullible Eve, Hilary was tempted. What would one night of extraordinary animal sex hurt? But Eve didn't end up with the devil; Eve ended up with Adam. The first dysfunctional family.

Hilary sighed.

She moved back until she felt safer. "I'm sure there are any number of girls who could help you get your rocks off, I'm just not one of them."

"It'd be fun," he said, still smiling in that come-to-me manner, still looking completely sure of himself.

"That's fun with a capital *F*, isn't it? And what happens when you're done? When I'm nothing more than a bad memory? And we have to work together? No, thank you."

He leaned forward and braced his elbows on his knees. "Is that all you're worried about? This is just a temporary gig for me. I've got to leave in August."

Temporary? She studied him for a minute, and all of a sudden she realized she was talking to Mr. Unreliable. Instead of giving him the door, like Dr. Tracy would tell her to do, she sat down.

On the chair, not the couch. She wasn't that stupid. But she was curious.

"Then why all the work? Why not be fat and happy and Director of Security, surfing the Web for four months on Daddy's payroll?"

Mr. Unreliable winced. "Nah."

"I really don't understand you."

He laughed. "Hilary, don't even try. You can help me, instead."

She curled her toes, waiting for the come-on. *Help me, baby.* "Help you how?"

"Teach me about the mattress business."

That wasn't a come-on. It sounded eerily legit. "What?" she asked, needing clarification.

"I want to learn it."

She frowned. "Shouldn't you be talking to your father?"

He studied the worn leather on her couch, the walls,

the ceiling, looking anywhere but at Hilary. "I have my reasons."

"How much do you know now?"

This time he met her gaze. "I've learned a lot about security. Corporate espionage. Protection of intellectual property. You know, the usual stuff."

"And nothing about beds?" she asked, shaking her head.

"I'm still learning."

He looked so well put together, so confident, yet in his eyes... "Why do you want to know?"

He shrugged. "It doesn't matter. Will you help me?"

It was that look that stopped her from saying no. He needed this, and she didn't understand why. "Maybe."

"Okay, you're having trouble with the concept. Let's make it easier. Your home needs a bit of work. A lot of work. We'll work a trade. During office hours, you turn me into a corporate mogul and when we're off the clock I'll make your house—" he frowned "—livable."

It was a good offer, but she felt she was missing the catch. Hilary leaned forward, noticing a tantalizing whiff of his cologne. Determined not to be waylaid by sensory onslaught, she shook off the effects of ninety-proof maleness. "There are going to be rules. The only springs getting sprung will be on the Dreamscape line. Capiche?"

If only her voice had sounded a little more forceful, not so—Mae.

He saw right through her and his smile returned, a blast of heat aimed in her direction. Hilary rubbed her arms, trying to get rid of goose bumps.

"Not unless you give me the green light. And Hilary, if you do flash it, well, I'm thinking it'd be a hell of a ride."

For a second she closed her eyes, envisioning all that he promised, remembering his kiss, his touch.

"Why are you really here?" she asked.

"I was worried about you," he said with wide-eyed innocence.

She wasn't buying it for a minute. "I'm fine. You can leave."

"Stubborn."

"Smart," she answered, and to prove her point, she stood and opened the door.

"Sadist."

Every now and then a woman has to take a stand. She would not be his doormat. Would not, would not, would not. She'd done that once in her life and that was enough. "Good night, Ben."

He came to stand beside her. He lingered close enough that she could feel him. All that heat, blissful heat. "Come out with me. Drinks. Someplace fancy."

The way he said "fancy" made her smile. So this was the way Texans talked. She'd heard his father say it just the same way. She looked him in the eye, wishing she could read minds, but instead she just settled for asking. "Why?"

"Because it's Saturday night and you should be outside in the real world rather than hibernating in your home."

She rolled her eyes, but already she was wavering. "Someplace fancy is the 'real world'?"

"Hell, yes. This is Dallas. Come on."

Hilary took in his khaki trousers, neat cotton pinstripe. He could wear a towel and it'd look great. Don't go there, don't go there, don't go there. She shook off the image. "I'd have to change clothes."

"Don't let me keep you."

Finally she nodded, letting the weakness of loneliness and the vision of him in a towel overcome her common sense. "All right. Just give me a minute."

It actually took thirty, but she considered it an investment. She dug out her one pair of boots and the little emerald linen sheath that made her look thin. After a brutal battle with her hair, she managed to tame some of the kinks. At least the weather was finally cooperating.

The look of appreciation in his eyes made her feel like a woman for the first time in several months. Maybe she'd like Texas after all.

Ever the gallant one, he opened the door for her. "Ready?"

She winked at him. Very Mae. "You betcha."

BEAU NASH WAS the snazziest place Ben knew to take her. Polished wood floors, bunches of flowers in every corner, and service that was quiet and unassuming. The wait staff probably knew more than the CIA, but you knew that these guys would never tell.

Ben would bet his last paycheck that Mark had never taken her to *snazzy*. When they walked in the door, Ben knew he was right.

He was determined to show her a good time. It was the least he could do in order to redeem his sex in her eyes, and maybe bring one of those rare smiles to her face. He liked the thought of that.

They took a table in the corner—the better to people-watch, and this was definitely a place for that pastime. The bar was packed, mainly with the glittering set of celebrities that adorned Dallas's top shelf.

He saw her watching a couple near the front. There was envy in her eyes. He realized he hated that.

"First date," he said, and the envy was replaced with confusion. Better.

"How do you know?"

"He's working too hard, she's nervous. No sex."

Now she smiled at him. Better still. "You can tell?"

"Oh, yeah." He spied another target. "See that couple over there, Black Jacket and Teal Strapless—they're living together."

She balanced her hand on her chin. "I can't wait to hear this one."

"There's no engagement ring—"

"They could just not believe in an outdated marriage

custom." She twisted the empty space on her finger as if her ring were still there, and her smile faded.

She had been engaged. He didn't have to be a mind reader to see that. "Did you have a ring?"

"Emerald-cut solitaire, modern setting, half a carat."

"Modern? I would have thought you were an old-fashioned type."

She shrugged. "He surprised me. Anyway, I'm more interested in Black Jacket and Teal Strapless."

Ben went back to work on her smile. "Black Jacket took a call on his cell phone. Definitely an established relationship. Rule number one. Never take a call when you're on a date."

The green eyes narrowed. "What if it's your boss?"

"No exception. The female takes priority."

"Your broker?"

"No exception."

"The president of the United States?" she asked.

"No exception. Besides, he's going to be 'Unknown' on caller ID." She laughed. If he'd thought she'd laugh again, he'd have hung up on the president.

She continued to press him. "World crisis. You're needed."

"What? They're going to put that on the caller ID?"

"But if you didn't take the call, then you'd never know what you missed."

Ben folded his arms across his chest. "So you're the queen of taking chances now?"

She thought for a minute, took a look around her. "Yeah, I am."

Still he didn't believe her. She continued to wear that shell-shocked hollowness in her eyes when she didn't think anyone was looking. "Why do I think those are just words?"

"You like analyzing everyone else's life, don't you? What about Ben MacAllister? If you were to analyze the illustrious life of Ben MacAllister, what would you say?"

Sitting under the glare of the interrogation light wasn't comfortable at all. But Ben managed a smile of his own. "First of all, illustrious is an overstatement."

"I don't think so. Taken from the viewpoint of a woman who spent her life in engineering, *your* life is definitely illustrious. You're dodging the question. Ben MacAllister, this is your life."

"Self-awareness is a weak spot for me. Besides, I'd rather talk about you. Here's an easy one for you, do you like camping?"

"Why?"

"No reason. Just curious if you're the outdoorsy type."

"Don't like to camp."

"Ah. School?"

"University of Tampa. Industrial engineering. You?"

"Stanford. English."

"No kidding? English? Why?"

"It seemed fun. Why engineering?"

Her brows drew together, and she thought. Obviously this was something she'd never considered before. "Can't say that it's fun. It's more of a serious career."

Serious career for a serious girl. He hid his smile and folded his hands on the table. "Greatest achievement?"

"Dean's list. Sophomore year. You?"

"Fourth-grade spelling-bee champ."

Their drinks arrived, and the serious conversations were over, much to Ben's relief. Instead, he spent the evening bringing out her smile as much as possible. He didn't know if it was his jokes, or the Cosmopolitan she was drinking, but she seemed happier. When they walked out of the restaurant, he felt the same exhilarating kick he got from skiing down the double-black diamond in the Alps. And while black diamonds were good, the kick in his heart—that was even better.

"YOU WANT ME to fix your front steps tomorrow? You can take me through the plans for the product launch after I'm done."

She leaned against the door, needing support. "You're actually serious?"

He shrugged. "Sure."

"Why?"

He moved in close. "Because. No other reason. Hilary, I've got to be straight with you. I'm going to kiss you good-night."

She heard a moan. Her own. It was very distinct, not to be confused with a sneeze or a cough—a moan. Moaning was not good. "I thought this was a business relationship."

"A business relationship?" he scoffed. "Oh, Hilary."

Hilary tried to look tough—a hard stance to manage when your legs were doing that Jell-O thing. "What makes you think I won't knee you in the groin until you start singing *Aida?*"

"That look in your eyes."

"There's death in my eyes. Look a little closer."

"And why are you scared of one little kiss?" He looked at her, carefully. "You can't forget, can you?" The heat had dropped. "Do you think about it, too?"

"No." She looked at the floor. "Sometimes."

He touched her chin with long fingers, tilted it up until she had to stare into his eyes. "I think about it, too. I remember how you felt in my arms, Hilary."

His voice lowered, deepened. He moved closer until their bodies were touching. Bliss.

She couldn't give in, she wouldn't give in. "And why is this all about you?"

"Do you want me to touch you? Is that why you're like this?"

"You should recognize this—go home, Ben."

"One kiss, and I'm outta here, Hilary."

"That's what it's going to take?"

He nodded. "Uh-huh."

He made it sound so simple, she couldn't help but agree. "All right. But just one."

She locked her arms at her sides, freezing them so she wouldn't turn into Clingy-woman.

Slowly, excruciatingly slowly, he lowered his head and met her lips. Her mouth betrayed her and clung to his. There was a promise in his kiss, a silky dream that was as fragile as the cobwebs she'd so brutally torn. Her head began to spin. It would be so easy to believe.

She wanted to trust him, wanted to believe he wouldn't hurt her, but how long would it take? How long before she was alone once more? One night? One week? One month? She pushed her doubts to a safer place, burying them deeply in her heart.

Just when her arms had lifted, just when she ached to touch him, he moved away.

"Good night, Hilary," he said, and then turned to the door.

"You mean you were actually telling the truth? You're leaving?" There was a small screech in her voice. An embarrassingly needy screech. Mae never screeched.

"Of course. You didn't think I was lying, did you? Well, hell, that'd mean you expected me to—"

She shoved him out of the house before he could finish.

The moonlight kissed his face, silvered his hair.

"See you tomorrow, Hilary."

A moan. She distinctly heard another moan. Damn.

SUNDAY AFTERNOON, Ben picked up Hilary for a thrilling shopping adventure at Home Depot. For Ben, home improvement fell under the "work" classification, rather than "fun"; however, it was a necessary evil, and he had never met a woman who needed more home improvement than Hilary.

Her house was still a mess, but that was something he could fix.

As they stepped into the world of plywood and nails, power tools and lawn and garden, Ben broached the question of the day. "So do you want cement steps or wood?"

"I think I'd like cement."

"It's more work," he said, trying to guilt her into wood.

She shot him one of those haughty looks. "Definitely cement. Is it expensive?"

He thought about lying, but he knew Hilary had money issues. If she wanted cement, well, cement it was. "It's not much. I can help you out if you need it."

"Thank you, but no. I would prefer to pay my own way," said little Miss Prim and Proper.

He couldn't help but smile. "We'll keep it cheap."

HILARY SPENT THREE marvelous hours trying to help but mostly ogled Ben while he assembled the frame for the steps and poured the concrete. There was something incredibly sexually arousing in watching a man do physical labor. Not only was she getting brand-new front steps, but she got a fantasy come to life on her very own porch.

She didn't tell him such things, tried to keep the un-adulterated lust out of her eyes. His ego was already big enough.

Secretly she'd already made her mind up. It had happened sometime between two and three o'clock, specifically when he took off his shirt. Did that make her shallow? Probably, but shallow and sated had a nice ring to it.

On a good day, he was hard to resist. On a day like today—the afternoon sun beating down on his broad back, sweat sliding between his shoulder blades—re-sistance was futile.

And why had she been resisting him? Surely she was mature enough, tough enough to handle whatever he threw her way. He was a no-strings kind of guy, well, she could be a no-strings kind of gal.

Just when she was about to lose all self-control and throw herself at him, he stood, rolled one broad shoul-der and then surveyed her steps with pure masculine pride. "You mind if I get cleaned up before we move to real work? I could use a shower."

Instantly she had processed the statement and kicked into analysis mode. He was going to take a shower, but there wasn't a do-you-want-to-join-me? invitation in his eyes. Chance of sex: ten percent. Hil-ary opened the door for him and said in her best of-course-I'm-not-thinking-carnal-thoughts voice, "Sure. Be my guest."

It was not her best effort. Mae would not be deterred by a lack of invitation; Mae made her own opportunities. Heck, Mae would have washed his back. Sadly, Hilary was not Mae. But all was not lost. The night was still young.

Ben brought in some clothes from his truck and then the torture began.

First he closed the door, but she didn't hear the click of the lock. Did she dare join him? No. Instead she sank weakly into her chair. Next, the sound of the water reverberated through the walls, bombarding her with images of him in her shower, water pouring down the powerful chest. Her mind panned slowly down his body—long legs, lean hips. Trails of soap would cling to his back, to the sharp line between his pecs.

Following her more elemental urges, she stood and went to the bathroom door. She could do this, of course she could. Chance of sex: eighty percent. Just when she had shucked her T-shirt, the water turned off.

Damn.

Chance of sex: zero percent.

In record time she had donned her T-shirt, flopped onto the couch, set her laptop on the coffee table, turned it on and opened the latest spreadsheet. When he emerged from the bathroom, fresh shirt and jeans, his hair endearingly tousled, she looked up expectantly. "Back so soon?"

He seated himself beside her, and she began to explain the marketing department's strategy for their new media campaign.

Ben stared at the document, looking completely fascinated.

Chance of sex: zero percent.

BEN LOOKED AT THE WORDS on the screen, reading them three times before they made sense. He had noticed the way she was watching him—the way her gaze collided with his approximately three times a minute. Yesterday, with her hands-off prickles firmly in place, he had thought it was fun to tease her, just a little hands-on finessing to remind her that yes, she was a woman, and yes, he was a man.

Now the fun was over.

He was downright randy and it terrified him.

Very discreetly he moved his burning thigh one inch away from hers. "Now, who is Tyler Campo?"

Looking completely frustrated with his lack of attention, she sighed, and his attention shifted from the screen to her chest. To make his groin throb even more painfully, she sighed again.

He looked up into green, green eyes that were alight with awareness and power. He nearly told her to stop it, but that would get him into a conversation that he wasn't ready to have so he repeated his question. "Who is Tyler Campo?"

"He's the lead reporter for *Bedding Magazine*. You

want him on your side at the conference. He needs to understand the potential that we see in the Dream-scape line. There's also Paul Angleton who writes for *Sleep Today*, and Leena Andrews who writes for the *ISPA News*."

If he could just focus on work...

Her thigh moved one inch closer to his and he almost jumped. At the last minute, he caught himself in time and simply gritted his teeth. Of course he could do this. However, when she leaned behind him for what he was sure was no other reason than to torment him, he faced the reality of their situation.

He had approximately four months left until August, four months until he left for Colorado. Now, in four months, he could spend approximately one hundred and twenty evenings warming the bed—scratch that, warming the couch—of Hilary Sinclair. Of course, that was assuming he was reading her current signals correctly, and he was pretty sure that he was. And then what would happen?

Here was a woman who had gotten out of a miserable relationship not so long ago, a woman who'd been engaged and still wore the scars. What sort of louse started an affair with a woman who was still in pain?

She shook her hair and he got a good whiff of her mango shampoo. That was all he could take.

"I need to go."

If there was disappointment in her eyes, he didn't

want to know about it. He stood, grabbed his coat, his keys and shot out of her house.

"Ben?"

He stopped on her porch, frozen, and she walked to the door, her hips swinging hypnotically. Her dark red lips tilted in a hint of a smile—not the sort of smile a woman nursing a broken heart would wear.

Ben winced. "I'll see you tomorrow."

The come-hither smile faded, all the pleasure in her face faded, and something in his cardiopulmonary region twisted. She held up a hand and gave him a half-hearted wave.

HILARY POKED AWAY at her keyboard, trying to find a comforting salve in her work. That was her destiny. No fairy-tale romances for her. Maybe she just needed to lower her expectations. She popped a mint in her mouth and switched from word processing to her computer poker game. Even an inside straight didn't give her the usual little thrill.

She got up to make some tea when she heard the squeal of tires and then a knock on her door.

Trying to keep a sharp rein on her imagination, she walked slowly and very methodically to the front door. If it was Ben, he had probably just left his coat, or had another question about the media campaign for the launch, or maybe he forgot a screwdriver.

Fifty million excuses stood on standby in her brain. Always be prepared.

She opened the door and a flood of desire poured through, enveloping her. He set his mouth on hers, her body pinned against the door, and the excuses were gone. Dear God, she wanted him.

His fingers thrust into her hair, holding her helpless. His breathing was fast, his broad chest rising and collapsing against the softness of her body. She had done this to him. She, Hilary Sinclair, had done this.

Hilary held tight and pressed closer. She needed to be closer to him. Her own heart pounded, but it wasn't breathing that concerned her. It was the exquisite sensation of his mouth. The pure desire—no, need—that she tasted on him.

He tore his mouth away and pressed his lips against her neck. "I shouldn't have left. I'm sorry."

She opened her eyes and stared into the darkness of the night, the emptiness of her street. "Come inside."

He didn't take his mouth away, merely pulled her away from the door and kicked it shut.

His hands thrust underneath her shirt, finding her bra. He didn't bother with the clasp, merely lifted the fabric out of the way until his hands could cup her bare breasts. Roughly he kneaded her flesh and she whimpered with relief, her head lolling to one side.

Her nipples burned under the heat of his touch and she arched back until she felt the safe lines of the wall. He wedged a hard thigh between her legs, his thick erection starting an ache low in her belly.

When he ground his hardness against her softness,

she slid inches lower, until only his thigh kept her upright. Her hands worked the buttons on his shirt, wanting to touch him. She parted the soft material, her fingers sliding up the hard planes of his torso, sliding up through the crisp curls that arrowed down his chest.

She shuddered in a moment of pure pleasure and then his mouth found hers and the storm began again.

Her ears began to ring, and she shook her head, trying to erase the annoying sound. He lifted his lips, just enough to whisper, "Don't answer it."

The phone. He sank back into the kiss, and for long moments she simply drifted on the liquid sensations that he was creating inside her. And then her answering machine kicked in.

"Hilary. This is Mary Lynn MacAllister. How're you doing? Listen, forgive me for calling, but I wanted to invite you and Tracy, Allen's wife, out for dinner."

BEN SIGHED and pulled away from Hilary. Nothing like your mother's voice to turn a near-perfect moment of sexual satisfaction into a cold shower. He watched as Hilary picked up the receiver and turned off the answering machine.

"Mrs. MacAllister, this is Hilary." She smiled weakly at him, her lips still swollen from his kiss.

"Well, sure I'd love to. When? What about Mr. MacAllister, would he want to come?

"Oh, I didn't know," she said, looking at him with eyes full of sympathy. Ben turned away. He hated that look. He didn't need her sympathy. Didn't need anyone's sympathy.

He buttoned up his shirt with shaking fingers.

"Of course I'd love to. I'll see you next Wednesday." She hung up the phone and held out a hand to him. "I didn't know."

He made it to the door before she could touch him. Right now he needed to be far away. "Yeah. See you tomorrow, Hilary."

This time he left, and he didn't come back.

ACCORDING TO HELGA, Sonny Bryan's had the best barbecue in Dallas. When Hilary first set foot in the old-style hole-in-the-wall, Hilary suspected Helga was right. Today Hilary needed all the help she could get, and she would lay good odds that Ben was a barbecue man. He had agreed to go to lunch with her after she told him she needed to discuss the latest test results from the Dreamscape line. In reality, she was worried about him. Each time she thought she had him figured out, he surprised her. Earlier, he had spoken so cavalierly about divorce, yet there had been nothing cavalier about the hurt in his eyes last night.

He looked completely normal today, wearing his no-worries smile as easily as his crisp white linen shirt. Now Hilary knew better. It was a foolish person who took Ben MacAllister at face value.

She ordered a cup of coffee, then after the waiter had

departed, flashed a no-worries smile right back at Ben. "So tell me what's good here."

"Onion rings, ribs, brisket sandwich."

Hilary tapped her finger on the laminated menus. Ribs were definitely out. Hilary steered clear of messy foods when in the company of the opposite sex. "What are you going to get?"

"Ribs."

Yeah, he probably wouldn't spill one drop of barbecue sauce on that white shirt. She shook off her critical tendencies and remembered why she was here. Bigger things were at issue than fabric stains, or lack thereof.

"I had a meeting with your dad today."

Ben looked up from the menu, his eyes alert. "Yeah?"

She played it cool, as if she didn't know what his father's opinion meant. "He wanted to know about the plans for Vegas."

He looked back down at the menu, his face a careful blank. "What did you say?"

"I told him you were a big help and that MacAllister Beds was going to do fine."

Under the shirt, she saw him draw a long breath. "Thank you."

When he looked up, she met his eyes. "It's the truth."

"I've had a good teacher."

A hot flush ran up her cheeks. She felt silly for letting

a simple compliment go to her head. She waved him off. "Oh, go on."

And he did. "No, I'm serious. You know your stuff."

It was the earnest look on his face, the sincerity in his eyes that stopped her protests. "Thank you." She took a sip of coffee. "How are you doing today?"

The earnest look disappeared. "Fine."

"You looked upset yesterday when you left."

"Nah. Too much caffeine," he said, looking as if what had happened was the last thing he wanted to discuss.

The waiter returned, took their order, and then disappeared.

Hilary wasn't done with the conversation. "You know, if you want to talk, I'm here."

"Nothing to talk about."

"Whatever you say." She didn't like his nonchalant tone, and she wished she could take away some of his concerns. "Your mom seems nice."

"She's the best."

Hilary leaned forward. "I'm excited about having dinner with her and Dr. Tracy. I can't believe I'm really going to meet her."

Ben laughed. "Want a Dr. Tracy mug? I've got three at my apartment."

"You think I'm silly, don't you?"

He didn't even hesitate. "Yes."

Hilary defended herself. "She delivers sound, sensible advice."

"Yeah, I bet you like that sound and sensible stuff."

Their food arrived, and she cut her brisket sandwich into small bites.

"Have you ever been sensible?" she asked, then took a bite of an onion ring that was as big as a fist.

"No. Sensible is code for boring."

What a guy. It wouldn't be too soon before he left town. "Is that why you're going to Colorado?"

"I don't stay in one place for too long."

"Yeah, that would be a dangerous thing, wouldn't it?" she asked, daintily picking up another bite of brisket.

"It's the way I am."

She heard the warning in his words, that Lone Ranger tone. What a fraud. He didn't want to admit he was human, but every now and then he let his guard down. "Why do you always sell yourself short?"

"Sometimes I'm right."

Slowly she shook her head. "I'm sorry."

"For what?"

"Your mom and dad. That's got to hurt."

He picked up a rib and stared at it for a long, long time. "Sometimes it does."

"Well if you need a friend, all you've got to do is whistle."

They finished the last of the meal in silence, and sure enough, he hadn't spilled a drop of sauce. Hilary looked down at her own coffee-splashed shirt and sighed. He smiled at her, making her forget all about her stain. "I can whistle pretty good."

She flashed him her best Mae look. "I bet I can make you whistle even better."

"You're a sly woman, Miss Sinclair."

"That I am. And don't you forget it."

EACH DAY BEN WENT to work, using his mornings to go over the manufacturing reports, studying the design specifications, looking through past invoices. Hilary would meet with him afterward, Starbucks cup in hand, and give him the lowdown on their competition, usually managing to spill a drop or two of coffee on the papers and on her shirt.

He kept his mouth shut.

Ben was amazed at her wealth of knowledge. His father was right. She was good.

He looked forward to their time together. He'd never had a good friend who was female. It had always seemed dangerous and he was never in one place for very long, but he liked Hilary. Liked her stubborn streak, her coffee stains, and the way she stared at the ceiling when she needed to think.

He had thought long and hard about the camping trip. But honestly, he had work to do. Each day he learned more and subsequently realized how little he knew about his father's company. He just didn't have the time, and if Hilary didn't like camping, well, that was one more reason not to go.

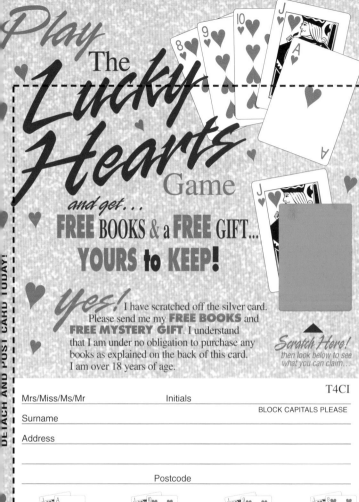

Play The Lucky Hearts Game

and get...
FREE BOOKS & a FREE GIFT...
YOURS to KEEP!

Yes! I have scratched off the silver card. Please send me my **FREE BOOKS** and **FREE MYSTERY GIFT**. I understand that I am under no obligation to purchase any books as explained on the back of this card. I am over 18 years of age.

Scratch Here!
then look below to see what you can claim...

T4CI

Mrs/Miss/Ms/Mr	Initials

BLOCK CAPITALS PLEASE

Surname

Address

Postcode

Twenty-one gets you
2 FREE BOOKS and a
MYSTERY GIFT!

Twenty gets you
1 FREE BOOK and a
MYSTERY GIFT!

Nineteen gets you
1 FREE BOOK!

TRY AGAIN!

DETACH AND POST CARD TODAY!

The Reader Service™ — Here's how it works:

NO STAMP NEEDED!

THE READER SERVICE™
FREE BOOK OFFER
FREEPOST CN81
CROYDON
CR9 3WZ

NO STAMP
NECESSARY
IF POSTED IN
THE U.K. OR N.I.

A major victory, at least in Ben's eyes, Spears came back with a substantially lower quote on both the fiber and the organic cotton as well. Ben celebrated by doing more home repairs.

That night he showed up at her door, tools in tow. "I need to fix the window frame."

"I could have been busy."

He noticed the playing cards on the table and the bag of Oreos as well. She didn't look busy—bored, maybe. "I thought about calling, but it just seemed to be wasting time. Besides, I wanted to ask you about the product plant in Mesa. It's running at seventy-seven percent capacity, and I think that seems low. What do you think?"

She looked up at the ceiling, staring in silence.

Finally he looked up, too. "You got another crack up there?"

"I patched one last week, but I think it's back. What are the numbers?"

He began to unscrew the old boards from the frame. "El Paso is running at eighty-three percent, Milwaukee at ninety-three, and then there's Mesa at seventy-seven. I think we can do something about that."

Furiously, she paced back and forth, sweats and T-shirt, and damned if she wasn't going without a bra. What started as typical male appreciation became a full-fledged boner. Hell. He faced the window so she wouldn't notice.

"Who's the product manager at Mesa?"

"A guy named Turner. He's been there for fifteen years. Dad says he's a good guy."

"Tell you what, tomorrow we go over the production reports. Maybe there's a trend."

And how could they fix it? Compensation? Ben settled in to pry the boards off the frame.

Their silence was interspersed by a voice from the radio.

"Dr. Tracy, this is Susan. I've had a boyfriend for about six years now, and I've been waiting for him to pop the question, but he just seems to be languishing around."

"Susan, hold on for just a moment. We're breaking for a commercial, but then I'll be back."

Ben hammered the old wood, using the noise to mask his snicker.

But Hilary heard him anyway. "What's so funny?"

He stopped and put down his hammer. "You really want to know? Six years. Come on, that's ridiculous. She should have been out of there after three months."

Hilary plopped down onto her couch. "Why three months?"

Ben picked up the screwdriver and unscrewed another screw. "A guy knows these things. After three months, a guy can tell if it's forever or not."

"I see. And how many 'forever' girls have you dated?"

He had to think about that question for a minute, and when he realized the answer, it wasn't pretty.

"None," he said, almost to himself. He thought of his father, the resulting divorce. Who had been the teacher, Ben or his father?

"Then why three months?"

Ben shook off his uneasiness. This was ridiculous. He stared at Hilary and then cracked a smile. "Because after three months I know they're not the one. Ergo, if I can tell they're *not* the right one, then I can tell that they *are* the right one as well."

"That's guy logic if I ever heard it."

Ben shrugged. "So? I'm a guy."

He went back to prying boards and she went back to listening to his sister-in-law. Ben rolled his eyes. *Women.*

HILARY TRIED TO LISTEN to Dr. Tracy, but it was nothing but commercials now. Besides, it was really Ben who had her full attention. After a few moments, she gave up the pretense and watched him with fascination, her chin balanced in her hand.

"You need some help?"

He looked over his shoulder. "Are you trying to insult me and my craftsmanship?"

"No, not at all." On to the question she was dying to ask. "Have you ever dated a girl for longer than three months?"

A single, casual shrug. "Sure," he said.

"Even though you knew she wasn't forever?" Hilary asked, just to be clear.

"Sure."

"Why?" Hilary asked, afraid to hear his answer.

"Sex."

"Sex?"

"Certainly," he said, not looking the least bit defensive.

"And you say that with pride?"

Ben laid down his hammer. "It's a primitive instinct that man has had for aeons. A man really needs to get laid. I'm not apologizing for it, Hilary. Any man that denies any of what I just said is lying. And I can tell you why he's lying, too. He wants to get laid and he thinks if he tells you some psychosensitivity you'll go soft on him."

She folded her hands carefully in her lap, her voice quiet. "Why are you telling me this?"

He carried on with annoying blithe. "You've got to be careful, Hilary. I don't want you to get hurt."

When she met his eyes, her smile was a little weak. "Yeah. Thanks. Let's see what Dr. Tracy has to say."

"Susan, six years is quite a long time. Has there been some reason the relationship has gone on this long? School? Career? Or financial obligations?"

"Well, no, but it never seems the right time."

"Susan, he's a loser. Dump him and find a man who's deserving of you. You can't blindly trust men. They must earn your trust. And be very wary of a man who makes lavish statements or promises in order to just part your thighs."

Ben's triumphant smile hurt the worst. Was this obvious to everyone but her?

She snapped at him simply because she hurt. "Okay, you might have been right just this once, but that doesn't mean that there aren't exceptions."

He didn't hesitate to answer. "He should have married her."

"Maybe he wanted to wait until they were a little more mature." It sounded lame even to her.

He picked up a nail and began to pound. "If he's been dating her for six years, and he hasn't committed to her, then he's using her."

As if he were the expert. Right. "What do you know about long-term relationships?"

"I dated a girl in Rio for nine months, once."

"This was the great sex?"

"She gave the best—"

Hilary waved her hand; oh, she did *not* want to hear this. "Enough. We'll agree to disagree."

Ben picked up another nail. "Any guy who strings a girl along for six years is a jerk, and any girl who puts up with it is a pushover."

A pushover. Hilary bit her lip. Hard. Her tears were long gone, but it was never easy facing one's own stupidity.

"Oh." Obviously the bright light had dawned for the genius. "How long?"

She swallowed the lump in her throat. "Seven years."

"I'm sorry."

It was the pity in his eyes that was slowly eating her up. She forced her voice to be perky, cheerful. "Why? 'Cause I was a pushover?" She even laughed.

He came and sat down on the couch. "No, because I didn't think."

"Mark was a habit to me. A date at the holidays, somebody to talk to after work. A way to avoid frozen dinners for one. Maybe I shouldn't have stuck around as long as I did. I was too comfortable to break it off. I made a mistake and I *hate* making mistakes."

His arm curled around her, comfortable and warm. She nestled closer to him, glad for his company. For a long time they sat in silence like that—Hilary feeling sheltered for the first time in her life. Dr. Tracy droned on in the background, dispensing sage advice, and then the programming progressed to late-night music. Eventually the announcer proclaimed it was midnight and Ben stirred.

"I should go. We can go over the production reports tomorrow morning."

"Oh, I forgot. Got a call with Susan at nine to go over the conference plans. Maybe when I get done with the call."

"Yeah, that sounds good."

He stood, his hands shoved in his pockets, looking for all the world as if he had something to say. Not the usual look for Ben.

"What is it?" she asked.

Ben met her eyes and she couldn't look away. "You're not alone, you know."

No, she wasn't. He'd been a good friend. She smiled at him, remembering all he'd done for her. "Thank you for the home restoration and for the company."

"Anytime."

"Well, you should go then."

He stood still. "Yeah. Night, Hilary."

"Night, Ben."

In slow motion, he lowered his head, clearly aiming for her cheek. A nice friendly kiss, nothing more. But then something flared in the blue of his eyes, a sensual pulse that echoed between her thighs. Hilary didn't move, simply stood there, waiting, as if she'd been waiting all her life.

This time he didn't disappoint her. His lips covered hers in a slow, leisurely exploration. Her sigh resounded in his mouth, almost a whisper. Through her veins, her blood slowed and warmed, and his arms curved around her, a sanctuary. Her sanctuary.

They stood for some time, a soft mingling of mouths and breath. Hilary drifted into the easy warmth that carried her away, pliant and needy. Tonight she couldn't resist. She needed his strength.

He didn't disappoint her. Together they sank into the cushions of the couch, his body covering hers completely. Under her exploring hands, his muscles tensed and hardened. Never had she been so aware of power restrained.

Purposefully his lips moved over her body, baring skin as he went. The air turned thick and hot, and she was drawn into a world she had never known. He was in no hurry, and her body strained impatiently. Instead of complying with her wishes, he laughed and turned his attention to her breasts.

The shadow of whiskers at his jaw were rough and coarse against her sensitive flesh, and each time she moved, the rasping sensation took her closer and closer to the edge of the precipice.

Her muscles began to quiver and ache, trying to find a release. His lips closed over her nipple and her head fell back as the first, slow climax washed over her.

Still, he wasn't done. His mouth drifted lower, tracing the line of her stomach, following the inside of her thigh. Once again she found herself shivering, and when he found her sensitive flesh he began to feast.

With shaking hands, Hilary pulled him up her body and kissed his mouth. "Now."

He didn't disappoint her. With one powerful thrust, he was inside her, filling her. She wrapped her arms around his strong back and held tightly, their bodies moving in concert.

The absolute rightness of it all frightened her. Ben was not Mr. Right, and he never would be—not for her. But then his mouth found hers, took hers in a long, slow kiss that matched the rise and fall of flesh against flesh, and she forgot to fight. Forgot to think. Instead she closed her eyes and let herself feel.

He drove into her one more time, and she felt the last climax close over her. This time he rose above her, watched her as she shattered.

Then his eyes closed, his body shuddered and collapsed. For a long time, neither moved. Then the world intruded. The air began to chill, the music turned to the late-night news, and Ben moved off her.

Her fantasy was over.

"I'm sorry, Hilary."

An apology. No declarations of love, not even, an "oh, baby" moment. She heard none of the words she so desperately needed to hear.

He pulled back, looking completely handsome, completely unruffled, and completely in control.

How did he do it? How did he remain so unaffected, while she was dangerously close to caring for him?

Not wanting to embarrass herself further, Hilary smiled and stretched. "Rule number one, never apologize after sex. It spoils the moment, if you know what I mean."

"You're okay with this?"

"Sure."

"I don't know." He began to pull on his clothes, and for the first time she realized that he'd worn a condom. She'd been so carried away that she hadn't thought of it. But Ben had.

She shrugged, as though nothing mattered to her. "So? You think I can't handle an affair?"

He studied her, and she forced her best vague expression. Finally he shook his head. "Nope."

"You're wrong."

"Maybe I am, but I don't feel right about this. Maybe I'm growing a conscience, maybe it's just because I like you. Hilary, you're different from anybody I've ever met. You're determined to be tough, but you're not."

"Yes, I am," she said, starting to feel naked. Reading her mind, he tossed her the old college sweatshirt she'd been wearing. She pulled it over her head, grateful for the warmth.

"Oh, come on, you're a cupcake."

A cupcake. Why couldn't she be the strong one, the tough one. Mae was tough. She looked at him and lied. "That's not true."

"I'm not going to hurt you."

"You can't hurt me, even if you wanted to."

"I'm trying to be honorable and noble, here, Hilary, not to mention live by all those other unsavory virtues, and you're making it very difficult."

Now she'd had enough. He didn't think she was strong and emotionless. He was wrong. "Go home, Ben."

"I think we should talk."

She tugged on her sweats and stalked to the door. Why could he get to her? "*Now* you want to talk? When it's about Ben, no talking allowed. But Hilary? Hell, let's get on *Oprah*."

"You're mad."

"Damn right I am. You don't make decisions for me."

He spread his hands wide, a gesture of helplessness. "I'm not trying to."

"Good night, Ben."

"I'll see you, tomorrow?"

"If you're lucky."

Then she closed the door and padded back to her couch. But instead of sleeping, she could only smell the faint scent of his cologne, the musky smell of their love-making, and under her hands she could still feel the strong warmth of his skin.

One tear fell, splashed onto her couch like a single drop of rain. She hadn't been a cupcake in Atlanta. She'd had a job she was good at, she had friends, a house that had no leaks and needed no repairs. Something in the water in Dallas had made her vulnerable, made her heart soft and turned her into a pile of emotional mush.

She didn't like that. Emotional mush made her susceptible to pain. Cupcakes got swallowed. Her heartbeat slowed and, as the clock ticked the minutes past, she tucked her heart deep inside her. By the time the sun rose, she hadn't slept much, but now she was certain the cupcake had disappeared.

6

ON SATURDAY NIGHT, Ben met Danny for a beer. He was determined to stay away from Hilary this weekend. He had work to do, reports to read and numbers to figure out. Every now and then, he took out the letter from the J&D ranch in Colorado, reminding himself of how much he wanted to do this.

Now it seemed like a lifetime ago. While waiting for Danny to appear, he watched the people in the dark bar, studying their moves—the coy gestures, the rituals that took place every Saturday night across the country.

At one time, he felt like he fit in here, but now he was struggling to fit in anywhere. His father didn't have any faith in him, and Hilary—he winced—why had he muddied the waters? Now there were memories he couldn't forget, images and sounds that kept haunting him.

Nothing had gotten any clearer by the time Danny sat down, sliding two beers along the table. "Glad you called."

"I decided not to go next weekend. Got work to do."

Hilary wasn't the outdoorsy type, but of course that had nothing to do with his reasons.

Danny leaned back in his chair. "Couldn't get a date, huh?"

Ben took a swig of his beer. "Nope. Struck out."

"What about the lady at the office?"

Ben met his eyes, steady and vague. "You want to know the truth? I've got work to do, okay? I'm going to be holed-up at MacAllister Beds until I understand every bolt and spring that makes up a mattress."

It sounded naive, even to his own ears, but he didn't want his dad to sell the company. Didn't want to face Hilary with failure.

Danny popped a pretzel in his mouth. "I'm disappointed. You were the last hold-out. The role model for all of us who had fond memories of the life we left behind."

Ah, jeez, just what he wanted to be—the role model for the Nike generation. "It's not a beer commercial, Danny, it's life."

Danny thwacked himself in the chest. "I'm dying here."

"I'm serious."

"And you think I'm not? Why the change of heart? You were an icon to us all, Ben. Why the sudden cravings for responsibility?"

Ben winced. He hated that word, but he didn't have an answer. "Because."

Ben watched as a smooth, banker type hit on a

blonde at the bar. It was easy to read the words, the body language. Nobody wanted to be alone. He rubbed his heart. For the first time in his life, he felt old.

Danny didn't miss a beat, all smiles and good cheer, buying drinks for a lovely brunette, charming the waitress out of her phone number.

Finally, Ben couldn't take it anymore. "I need some advice. Remember the girl you dated in college—Diane? She had just come off a breakup, right? How'd you handle it?"

"I told her up-front that I still had law school to go through and that it was my first priority. I left the choice up to her."

"And she was okay with that?"

"Yeah."

"And?"

"We broke up."

"How'd that go?"

"There was screaming involved." Danny shook his head. "I really liked her, too."

"You ever look her up?"

"I saw her a couple of years ago, but she refused to talk to me."

That's what he was afraid of. That she wouldn't talk to him anymore. Hilary was an all or nothing girl, and Ben had never been an 'all' kind of guy. And the thought of staying, finding out exactly what was inside him, was even scarier. "I like her," he said, first to himself, and then aloud.

Danny frowned. "Diane?"

"Hilary."

"So what's the issue? Once they reach the age of consent, you are thereby resolved of all responsibility."

"You're a moron."

"Ah, but I'm a sexually satisfied moron. And therein lies the beauty."

Danny had it easy. He knew where his life was headed. He'd already proved himself in the real world. That was a test Ben had always walked away from. It was easier to climb mountains, play cowboy, or run moguls in the Alps.

And what if that was all he was? A paperback cowboy who couldn't cut it anywhere else. He laughed at himself, burying his fears in the cold tang of beer. "I can't do that to her. She's vulnerable."

"Drink another one, Ben. It'll help."

HILARY SPENT her Saturday afternoon painting her kitchen cabinets a cheery yellow, anything to keep her mind off Ben. Sadly, Dr. Tracy didn't work weekends. Instead, Hilary turned her stereo to the country and western station. As the clock struck seven, she was pouring her fourth glass of wine—when the phone rang.

Her heart started pumping fast and she made herself practice her breathing. Mae never waited around by the phone. Mae was no cupcake. Hilary waited the requisite three rings before she picked up. "Hello?"

"Hil, it's Laura. How's Texas?"

Hilary studied the ceiling, counting the cracks. She shouldn't be disappointed because it was only her best friend from Atlanta. *Only.* How weak was that? Her best friend was now an *only.* No, no, no. Hilary smiled. Laura couldn't see that, but it mattered to Hilary. "Texas is hot, but at least the rain has stopped. What are doing home? I would think you'd be out with Scott."

There was a long sigh. "We broke up. No sparks, you know? I'm not bummed, but I am going to take a few weeks off before I'm officially available again. Maybe I'll go shopping. New shoes, new dress, new blood. How 'bout you?"

Disappointed. She was definitely disappointed. "Oh, Dallas is great. You should come out and visit."

"How's the new house?"

"Wonderful. I feel just like Martha Stewart. I'm going to make drapes," she said, thinking that she would eventually, but she'd have to fix the rest of the window frames, first.

"Well, don't get yourself too settled down there. I fully expect you back home in one-point-five years. That's enough time for you to work out that wild hair and return home to your friends where you belong."

Home. A wave of homesickness swept over her as she stared at the miserable domicile she presently resided in. This wasn't home. It would be so easy to pack it all in. She could sell the house, go back to Atlanta.

Where she belonged. Life was easier in Atlanta. No lonely Saturday nights. Why, if she were there right now, she and Laura could paint the town red.

"Maybe," was the best answer she could come up with.

"Mark took your old house off the market. Said he just couldn't part with it."

Damn the man. How dare he live in their house? He probably was going to have sex there, too. In her bed. The specially designed adjustable posturepedic with dual controls. And all the while, she was sleeping on a couch that wouldn't know an innerspring if it bit it. She rubbed her eyes, practicing her deep breathing. "Oh, well, that's his right. It is his house."

"I think he's missing you, Hil."

"Well, then I guess he shouldn't have dumped me." Reality intruded and she noticed a cobweb in the corner.

"If you came back..." Laura's voice trailed off.

"Are you kidding? Right now I'm fighting these Texas boys off with a broom," she said, using her mop to attack the silvery threads.

"I miss you, Hil. We all do."

She had thought the move would be exciting, a new adventure, a means to run away. Now she was tempted to run right back. "Keep good thoughts, Laura."

"What does that mean? Something's wrong, isn't it?"

Hilary leaned on her broom and stared critically at her home. Her dream of a 27" TV had ended up being just that—a dream and her love life was—she sank down on the couch—her love life was rocky, to say the least. "It's not exactly like I imagined."

"Well, of course not. It's Texas. Remember what you said? The great frontier?"

Yeah, she had said that. She jabbed at the floor with the broom. An adventure. She wanted to prove to the world that she was tough. Tough women didn't get dumped. Tough women didn't feel pain. "Thanks, Laura."

"For what?"

"You just reminded me of something very important."

"What's that?"

Hilary leaned back against the couch. "I am Mae."

ON SUNDAY AFTERNOON, Ben made the long trek to North Dallas. He didn't have a choice. He walked up the three flights of stairs, all the while shaking his head. Why had she picked an apartment with stairs? What if her arthritis kicked in?

He had bought daisies simply because he thought he should bring something. After all, she'd lived here for three months, and this was his first visit.

But mothers weren't supposed to live in apartments.

When she answered the door, she looked the same, maybe even happier. "Ben?"

"Hi, Mom. You don't have to sound so surprised."

"No, come on in."

He looked around the small apartment, noticing the new dining room table, the new flowery-print sofa, and the old curio cabinet in the corner, filled with her birds and all the old Hummels.

Everything looked wrong, out of place. The cardinal perched on the log should have been sitting on top of the mantel, and the little girl with the shy smile and the stack of books belonged on the round table next to his grandmother's lamp. He jammed his hands into his pockets. "It must have taken you forever to move all that stuff up here."

"The movers were very nice."

Movers. His own mother had hired movers. Why hadn't he thought about these things? "I could have helped."

"You were busy."

Oh, yeah. He was busting his butt playing poker in a Vegas tournament. "Not that busy," he said, seating himself in one of the hard dining room chairs. It suited his mood.

"It's all water under the bridge. Want some tea?"

"Nah."

"So to what do I owe this unexpected pleasure?"

"I hadn't seen your new digs yet. Figured it was time I paid you a visit." He handed her the flowers. "Here."

"My, my," she said, sniffing the flowers extravagantly.

"How do you like it?" he asked. "It's not exactly home, is it?" He noticed the way she'd hung her pictures on the wall rather than putting them on top of the old piano. His fingers itched to rearrange it all.

"No. I feel like I'm starting over." She plucked a vase from inside her cabinet and filled it with water.

"Dad shouldn't have been a jerk to you."

"Ben, stop that. This divorce was a mutual decision."

He watched her arrange the flowers, her thin hands moving deftly. "It's me, Mom."

When she looked back at him, there was cool acceptance in her eyes. "It's the truth."

"All right. We'll play it your way." He opted to change the subject. "You going to take Hilary out to dinner on Friday?"

"Well, I had to see what everyone was talking about."

"Who's been talking about her?"

She smiled the same old smile, and then sat down on her new couch. "You."

"Oh. Yeah, well, she's in a bad place right now."

"Oh?"

At that moment, Ben was glad Hilary would meet his mom. If Hilary would just clue in, she'd realize that she needed a friend, someone who would listen to her, someone who could give her advice.

And that someone wasn't him. He forced a smile. "It's not my place to say anything, just be nice to her."

"Benjamin, have you ever known me to be anything but?"

"Well, no." The walls, covered with reminders of his old life, started to close in. "You been looking at houses?"

Her face lit up. "Some. Found a nice little two-bedroom with a garden in back. I always wanted a garden. Now I can have one. Your father never believed in pesticides. Stubborn man."

"If you need any help with it, you call. I can help you. If you need anything—"

She cut him off. "Ben, I can take of myself, thank you for offering. I'm even having my own Fourth of July party this year."

"We're not going to do the barbecue?" The party was a MacAllister tradition. His dad would hover over the grill, his mom would brew sweet tea, and then there were the fireworks in the park.

"Your father is having one. I'm having my own shindig. Inviting the neighbors over for margaritas. You should come."

Margaritas? "Maybe."

"Tell me about Hilary."

"Not much to say," he answered, studying the flowered print on the sofa.

"Do you have feelings for her?"

Ben had always had an open relationship with his mom, could tell her anything in the world, but today something stopped him. "We're friends," he said. It wasn't the complete truth, but Ben didn't know the complete truth himself. In fact, he didn't want to know.

"I see," she said, using that same "yeah, right" kinda voice that Tracy had used. "You seem very concerned about her."

The walls closed in a little tighter. "Mom, she's not the right kind of girl for me. She's nice, sensitive, high maintenance. It'd be you and Dad all over again."

"I resent being called 'high-maintenance,' and you're not your father."

"I never thought we were alike until now." Ben shrugged it off. "Besides, I've got the list."

"Ah, yes. The list. How's it going? What's next?"

"A ranch in Colorado."

Her eyebrow rose. "Aren't you getting a little old for cowboys and Indians?"

"And what do you think I should do?"

"What do you want to do?"

He closed his fingers, tight, feeling like he was thirteen all over again. More than a boy, not quite a man. "I don't know."

His mother slapped his knee, a little sharper than he deserved. "Well, you've got lots of time to decide. Hell, I'm sixty-three and I'm trying to figure out what I want to do, too."

That brought a frown to his face. "Mom, you shouldn't cuss."

"That was your father's rule, not mine."

Ben started to laugh. "You're cracking me up, Mom."

"You think I'm joking?" she asked, looking dead serious.

He turned to her, horrified. "You are, aren't you?"

Then her face broke into a smile. "Gotcha, my boy."

He was going to have a heart attack soon. Time to leave. Ben got up and hugged her. His mom, the cutup. He'd loved her all his life and just now realized he didn't know her. "I love you, Mom."

"I love you, too, Benjamin."

He started for the door. "Gotta go. I expect a full report after your dinner."

"I'll tell you every detail. Although if she finds some nice young man to take her home, my lips are sealed."

Ben jerked his head around. For the second time in one day he'd experienced a sharp kick in the gut.

But his evil mother only stood there grinning.

"Gotcha again."

By THE TIME Hilary had her call with Susan, the day had not gone well. Ben had been seemingly busy. She didn't seek him out, merely made several pointed trips to the break room, which happened to be across from his office. Then, after lunch, things got worse. The schematics for the latest design had somehow gone back a version, Martin MacAllister had been walking through the company in silence, nodding his head ominously.

As she greeted Susan on the phone, she couldn't

help but think the woman sounded chipper for some-one with four pins in her leg.

"How're you feeling?" Hilary asked.

"Pain medications are good. Leg hurts like hell, though."

"Sorry."

"The accident was my fault. Never talk on a cell phone in a car. But it'll heal. How's the project going?"

Hilary brought up her notes on the screen and smiled. "Interviews are set up."

"Tyler Campo?"

"Check."

"Leena Andrews."

"Check."

"Got the draft press release?"

"Check."

"Fax it over, and I'll critique it for you."

Hilary added the task to her to-do list. "Okay. I need some quotes. Got any ideas?"

"You haven't talked to any of the usual suspects?"

"No, was I supposed to? Who are the usual sus-pects?"

"Sweet Mary, I forgot to tell you. Call Summers in Chicago and Phillips in Los Angeles. They're always good for it."

Hilary had flashbacks to the time in second grade she forgot her homework. It had only happened once, but that had been enough. "Who?" she asked.

"Carol Summers and Matthew Phillips. Ask Martin's secretary for their contact info. Bring them into Dallas and they'll do you right.''

Hilary added another task to her list. "Anything else?''

"How much booth space did you reserve?''

"Four and one-half.''

"Needs to be more. We don't want to look cheap or crowded. Go for seven.''

Furiously Hilary typed in her notes. "Seven. Got it.''

"Has the media firm come back with a proposal on the brochures?''

"What media firm?''

"Oh, that's bad. Eight weeks out, though, we've got time. It's Taylor Graphics. Call Chuck Taylor and have him express what he's got to me. What sort of giveaways have you come up with?''

Hilary sank down into her chair, scrunching her toes until it hurt. "Giveaways?''

"Yeah, you know, buttons, pens, T-shirts.''

"Susan, I'm an engineer. We don't think of the world in terms of tchotchkes.''

"Hilary, for now, you're marketing.''

"Marketing, oy. Okay, tell me what else I've overlooked.''

For thirty minutes Hilary took notes and by the time the call was over, she had fifteen pages of things to do.

It was going to be a long night.

IT WAS SEVEN O'CLOCK when Ben found her in her office, swearing at her computer.

"One day the computers are all going to unionize, and then you won't be able to abuse them anymore." Hilary looked up, and he noticed the lines of fatigue that scored her forehead. Even her hair drooped. "Long day?" he asked, already ruining his promise to himself to keep things casual.

"Got that right." Tentatively she smiled at him, her eyes full of questions. "I've got a brochure to flesh out. The graphics company has no idea what I'm talking about. They didn't even know about the job."

Ben pulled up a chair to her desk. Closer than he needed to be, but this was one area he could help. "Can I make a suggestion? I'll take you to get a cup of coffee. I do my best work on cocktail napkins. I bet we can come up with something in a few hours."

She avoided his eyes, leafing through the pages in front of her. "I talked to Susan today."

Ben took the hint and followed the change of subject. "How's she healing?"

"Good, but not fast enough." She ran a hand through her hair, pushing it out of her eyes. "I should stay here and see if I can finish this."

He hated to see her look so beat. This was a battle he wouldn't let her fight alone. "You've been sitting here for how long?"

"About five hours."

He tried not to smile. "Not done yet?"

"No."

Ben stood, put his hands on her desk, trying for an

authoritative yet professional demeanor. "And how many hours will you sit there until you decide you must go home?"

"Seventy-two."

Hilary made authoritative difficult. "The strain has fried your brain."

Finally, a weak smile emerged. "I'm only going to stay thirty more minutes," she offered.

Ben put a light hand on her shoulder, wishing she would lean on him, even just a little. "And what is thirty more minutes in the big scheme of things? We can crank it out before the check comes. Would you love a cup of coffee?"

Her response was pure Pavlov. "Coffee? Venti non-fat latte?"

He had her now. "Decaf or leaded?"

"What time is it?"

Ben checked his watch. "Seven seventeen."

"Definitely decaf."

THEY ENDED UP at Fountain Place, having coffee and something with chocolate drenched in raspberry sauce. He made Hilary order decaf. He knew that look. She wanted to zip through all of Susan's list in one night. They fleshed out the bare bones of the brochures, enough to give to the graphics company. Tomorrow he could help her with the other stuff, but right now it was after ten and she needed to be home. In bed. Alone.

He insisted on following her home. Safety reasons only, of course. And then he followed her in, simply to check and make sure the place looked safe and dry.

Not wanting to put his hands on her, he jammed them into his pockets. It seemed best.

She offered him a drink of water and had just gone into the kitchen, when he noticed a red light blinking on the answering machine. "You got a message."

"Oh, good," she called from the other room. "I bet it's Dr. Tracy, oops, sorry, Tracy. Punch it and see."

Ben was still shaking his head when he hit the play button.

"Monday, nine thirty-four p.m. Hilary, it's Mark."

Ben turned his head and stared at the little white machine. "I'm not sure you're wanting to talk to me right now. But I was having lasagna tonight—Monday, can you believe it—and was just thinking about you. Call me. You know the number."

The little prick.

"Who was it? Was it Tracy?" Hilary asked.

"Wrong number," he said loudly, his finger poised over the delete button.

Her day had been hard enough, and now this.

The conscience was a tricky thing. It was easy to believe what he wanted to do was best for her, easy to rationalize it all away. However, the truth was much simpler. He wanted Mark as far away from Hilary as possible, and phone lines were much too personal.

A little voice whispered for him to send the message

to virtual purgatory and he was just ready to press the button when she walked into the room, glass in hand. "Wrong number?"

"Yeah." Ben cleared his throat. "Hilary?"

"Hmm…" she said, her finger poised over the play button.

He grabbed her hand. "If you need me for anything, you know you can count on me, right? If you just want to talk or need a shoulder for something."

"Sure," she said, completely dismissing him. And then she listened to her messages.

When she got to Mark's message, her face turned pale.

"Hilary…I can stay."

She crossed her arms over her chest, but the light of battle was gone from her eyes. "No. I really need to be alone."

"Hilary. Don't call him back."

"Thank you, but I didn't ask for your advice on my love life."

She was going to call him. *Damn.* "I'm trying to help you."

"There you go again, doing that helping thing. I'm a big girl, I can take care of myself. Go, Ben."

He threw up his hands. "Okay, fine," he said, and stalked outside.

How on God's green earth could he possibly prove that she needed him? How did he know? This was all uncharted territory for him, something that worried him a hell of a lot more than number thirty-seven on his "things to do before I die" list.

But he couldn't give up; that much he did know.

He turned around.

"Hilary…" he said again, but she had already closed the door.

HILARY REPLAYED THE MESSAGE eight times. She had expected it to hurt more, but somehow on a late Monday night, when she was about ready to drop, it seemed to hurt less. She didn't know if she would call Mark. Part of her wanted to ignore the message, pretend it hadn't happened. But then he'd think that she was too traumatized to have one little phone call.

And she didn't want that. At the same time, she didn't want to just pick up the phone, call him, like a dependable doormat.

It was time to take charge of her life. Go for the gusto. Mark was beef stew and Ben was dessert, definitely dessert. If there was one thing Hilary believed in, it was always eating dessert first. Now it was time to give in to her cravings.

She picked up her bag of cookies from the kitchen and flopped on the couch. Life was easier with an Oreo in your mouth. Finally she made her decision. She picked up the phone and dialed.

After three rings, the voice answered. The quiet voice that could always make her feel better.

"Hi, Mom. How're you doing?"

She kicked back. The men in her life could wait awhile. She needed to talk to Mom.

7

BEN LOOKED at his watch. Nine thirty-seven in the morning.

She was late.

Ben had spent most of last night watching bad cable and pacing the small confines of his lackluster apartment. Hilary was strong—on most days she had a spine. Most of all, she had Ben.

She didn't need Mark. He picked up a Hi-Liter, prepared to go through the latest quarterly report.

He tried to concentrate, but the words in front of him started to blur. Where was she?

At ten, he was ready to call the cops. He had been by her office four times—*four*—and she still hadn't made it in.

Maybe her car had died. She could have called him if she needed a ride into work. He'd go get her. He picked up the phone, ready to dial, and then put it back down.

No, he wasn't going to let it bother him. She could take care of herself, he thought to himself, and ignored the fact that it bothered him.

Instead he went back to studying his report. Just

when he'd almost immersed himself in the ever-fascinating study of mattress design, she sashayed into his office, a woman without a care in the world.

And why was that?

She had ditched the white shirts and plaid skirts in favor of some Saks-looking suit that clung in all the right places. Her hair was piled up on her head, exposing what he had never realized was a deliciously tempting neck. Trouble, definitely trouble.

Ben frowned at her. "You're late."

She looked at her watch and made a little moue with her dark red mouth. "Oh, I guess I am."

"Do you have a minute?" he asked, wondering if that smile had something to do with Mark or whether it was just a smile because it was Tuesday morning.

Yeah, right, Ben.

She settled into the chair across from his desk and crossed her legs. Her sensible black shoes were gone. In their place were these designer, one-of-a-kind tall, sexy things.

Ben scowled, feeling the start of a headache.

"What can I do for you?" she asked, staring him right in the eyes.

Immediately the hairs on the back of his neck stood up. He cleared his throat, desperately wanting to ask about her personal life but not about to do it, as a matter of principle. "I have a question. If I'm understanding this right, it costs us about thirty-two cents a spring for the helicals, but the innersprings only run twenty-four cents. Now, it seems to me that it wouldn't cost much more to put in a few more helicals here," he said, pointing to the diagram that he'd drawn out.

Hilary leaned over his desk, showing him more flesh than he'd seen in his dreams, and he fought to breathe.

It was a struggle to look up into her face, but when he did and saw the devil in her eyes, he could feel the yawning jaws of the trap she was laying for him.

Hilary Sinclair, seductress extraordinaire. It was a new look for her, but she didn't seem to have any qualms about it.

On the other hand, Ben had about eight inches of qualm. Not his finest moment.

He rolled his chair back a few feet. "What do you think?"

With a slow sweep of her hand, she picked up his Hi-Liter and then tapped it on the notepad. "Yeah, but the innersprings support your back here." She arched back over his desk, a pose he'd seen practiced at various topless clubs with much less finesse, and pointed her chest right up at the sky.

Ben looked up just as Helga walked in and cleared her throat. Hilary flung herself in her chair, her face a deservedly attractive shade of red.

"Mr. MacAllister," Helga snapped, disapproval oozing in her voice, "you have a call with Wilson Warehousing scheduled in an hour. Should I arrange for it here, or in your father's office?"

"I'll take it here, Helga. Thanks."

Hilary straightened her skirt and then raised her chin, all business again. "I'd like to sit in, if that's all right."

Ben smiled, happy to see the old Hilary return. One disaster averted. "Of course, Miss Sinclair."

Helga turned. "Very good, Mr. MacAllister, Miss Sinclair."

After she left, Ben burst out laughing.

Hilary's heels tapped out a fast beat on the floor. "That wasn't funny."

"I gotta disagree."

"It's rude to laugh at the expense of another person."

He wiped the smile off his face. "You're right. I'm sorry. Let's talk springs."

It was a testament to his iron will that he kept his eyes stuck on her face. She seemed to have abandoned her earlier, more gutter-minded thoughts. And although most of him was relieved, parts of him were disappointed.

Sorely disappointed.

They started a spirited debate on the benefits of the extra helicals and Hilary stood her ground. "You just don't understand."

"No, I don't."

"Come here." She grabbed his hand and led him out of his office.

"Where are we going?"

"The lab. I'll show you exactly why it wouldn't work." She sped to the research center, all business.

Then she pushed open door number six. The newest member of the Dreamscape line.

"Pay attention, 'cause I'm serious now," she said, and then sat on the bed.

She looked up at him, so earnest, so sincere, and he worked hard to keep his eyes glued to her face rather than the long line of cleavage that was playing peeka-boo every time she moved.

"I'm listening," he said, thinking he could count her freckles, or something.

She bounced on the bed, her freckles bouncing with her. Unfortunately she had no freckles.

He winced.

"You see this give?"

Ben nodded.

She bounced three more times. Ben glanced around the room for a chair. Man, he needed to sit down.

Shit.

Very discreetly, he placed his notepad in front of him.

"Now, if you put the helical springs here—" she sprawled across the bed and pointed to the edge, then looked ahead, eye level with the notepad that jutted suspiciously at a nice forty-five-degree angle "—the play in the bed goes away, and the mattress is just—" she swallowed "—hard."

Ben moved back a couple of steps, back from those wide eyes. "I'm not going to apologize. This is your fault."

"Have you heard a word I said?"

"Yes. You bounced a few times, and talked about how an extra row of helicals would turn the mattress hard."

"That's close." She sat up, noticing how his eyes kept flickering to the gap in her blouse.

"You can't be mad at me," he said, unwilling to take unwarranted blame. "I'm the victim here."

And did she take pity on him? No, instead she slid off the bed slowly, very, very slowly, exposing the dark edge of her stockings.

He tried to speak, tried to warn her away, but his hands and voice refused to function.

She slunk toward him, her hips swaying in a hypnotic rhythm.

"Hilary..." he said, moving back one more step. He had started this day with good intentions, but now he'd forgotten what they were. Hell, he'd forgotten his own name.

"Ben..."

Her sultry voice woke him up and he took another step back. "We're not doing this, Hilary."

She pursed her lips, got a little baby-doll look in those wicked green eyes. "No?"

And then she raised her arm.

Oh, God, she was going to touch him.

Instead, her arm reached beside him and pushed the door closed.

Trapped. Trapped with a madwoman intent on seduction.

And to be honest, there were worse ways to go.

"I told you this was a bad idea," he started, trying to sound sincere.

"I'm going to forget you said that."

This whole situation screamed setup. "No, I'm not going to let you...let me—"

"Ben, Ben, Ben..." Her hand slid up his chest. "Do you remember what you said? You said I wasn't tough enough. I'm here to tell you that I am."

And she looked it, too. Damned if she didn't look the part of a woman who could stamp all over a man and take him to heaven six ways to Sunday all at the same time.

But this was Hilary. He needed to slow down.

But he was then hit with a flash of inspiration. All he needed to do was ask her out. After a date, sex was fair game. Yet, this was on-the-job sex. That called for something extra. "Do you like to dance, Hilary?" he asked, praying that she'd say no. Jeez, he hated to dance.

"No," she whispered, her lips feathering his ear. Then she drew back. "But if you need an out, there is something."

His hand reached over, waiting for the green light just to touch her. "What?" he asked urgently.

"I want to learn the tango."

"Huh?" he asked, his fingers a mere quarter of an inch from her breast.

She pulled back farther. "Tango. You know," and she began to hum a few bars.

Ben closed his eyes, tasting a rose between his teeth. "Oh, no."

"But it's so...stimulating," she said, rubbing against him in a brazen manner.

For that he could certainly handle a rose. "Okay, we'll do whatever you want."

"Tonight. Lesson at seven o'clock," she answered, just before she kissed him.

The temperature in the room rose a thousand degrees and he wasn't willing to wait. Ben pulled her back to the bed, his mouth never leaving hers. "Tell me about the springs again. That was so cool," he murmured against Hilary's lips, pulling her down on top of him.

His fingers fumbled with the clasp on the front of her bra, and he pushed away the nothingness of her shirt. She unbuttoned his shirt and tossed his tie over his head. "Does the door lock?" she said, and he struggled with comprehension.

Comprehension came in a big, dark cloud. "No."

"As Director of Security, that's an oversight you should rectify...tomorrow," she said, her voice husky.

With a sad heart he began to refasten her bra.

"What are you doing?"

"Putting you back together," he said, adding a long-suffering sigh for extra sympathy points. Still, he had been able to keep his promise, and he hoped she appreciated that.

She sat back on her knees, her breasts still fitting nicely in his hand. "And why is that?" she asked, as if he were a slow child.

Oh, she was a wicked, wicked woman.

For a moment he weighed the possibilities. Getting caught by one of his colleagues, or even worse his dad, and losing all vestiges of respect vs making love to Hilary.

It was no choice at all.

"Hilary, you naughty girl," he said, shaking a finger at her.

"Come closer, and I'll show you how naughty I can be."

It took about one second for him to throw her shirt across the room, raise her skirt around her waist and unzip his pants.

Only to discover that the research lab didn't come equipped with condoms.

Ben sat, Hilary in his arms, poised on the brink of ultimate sensual bliss and swore.

"What's wrong?" she asked.

"I'm sorry." For the second time, he began to put her back together. Man, his body couldn't take this sort of torment twice in one day.

Her smile was his first clue.

She reached into her pocket and waved the foil packet in front of his nose.

"Ta-da."

Any last-minute doubts that this was an entirely innocent little rendezvous were completely tossed out the window. "You set me up," he said, trying to sound indignant.

"Uh-huh," she said, and ripped the wrapper open with her teeth. "Want me to put this away?"

As he stared into her deep green eyes, he realized that there were times a man had to stand up for honor and righteousness, show that he had backbone.

Today wasn't one of those times.

Who has he kidding? He could never resist her. "Woman, bite your tongue."

"Glad you're seeing things my way."

She quickly put the condom on him and after an eternally long two seconds, he had her straddled on his lap and then he was inside her.

While he waited for his heart to slow, he simply closed his eyes and went completely still.

Then he opened them and let himself drown in her gaze. He knew he was in trouble. He knew she was in trouble. But right now nothing seemed more important than making love to Hilary.

And so he did. He moved slowly, holding her hips in his hands, watching her.

She didn't cling to him, didn't hold tightly. Instead,

her fingertips barely grazed his chest. But her eyes were full of questions, and he nearly turned away.

Not this time.

She was the first one to look away, but he tilted her chin, made her look back.

"Last time we did it your way. This time we do it mine."

When she stared up at him, he saw so much vulnerability, so much uncertainty. He brushed his lips over hers, once, twice, and then lost himself in her kiss.

Someday they were going to do this right. In a bed, his, hers, he didn't care. He wanted skin against skin.

"Hilary," he started, just as a door slammed.

They both stopped. She started to get up; he held her tight. "Shh," he whispered in her ear.

Outside the room, he heard his brother's voice as he wandered in the hallway. For a while Allen would speak, and then stop. He was on the phone.

Ben tuned out his brother and smiled. They were home-free.

He looked at Hilary and nodded.

Furiously she shook her head.

He nodded, and this time he ignored her and started to move again. After all, this had been her idea. It seemed easier to blame her for his own weakness. He didn't like analyzing his own desires.

"Ben," she whispered, and he kissed her just to shut her up. He felt her fists tight against his back, and then relaxed.

Eventually she yielded, her hands balanced on his shoulder, sliding her breasts against him. The first time she did, he almost came.

Not having one bit of that, he shifted them until she was lying underneath him. Once more he was in control.

This time he took one of her nipples into his mouth, pulling in time to their lovemaking. Low noises came from her throat, music to his ear.

"Better, Hilary," he murmured, tasting the silk of her skin. "But still not enough."

He maneuvered a single finger between them, coming up tight against their joined bodies. This time he watched her eyes as he touched between her slick folds, slowly, surely. He circled her, watching her eyes widen. Her hips ground against him, and again he nearly lost it.

"No, no, no," he whispered.

This time, he was more intent, feeling her buck each time he touched her. Her movements became more frenzied.

For a heartbeat he let his body bask in the pleasure; she was close. She buried her lips against his shoulder, muffling her sounds. He touched her one last time. Her body bucked again and her teeth sank into him. The pain pulled at the last of his control. He gave in to his climax, feeling the room spin, and he dragged in a breath.

The room stopped moving and he let the sounds

wash over him. Hilary's even breathing, his brother's conversation...

What?

Then he remembered.

Hilary stiffened beneath him and he rolled to one side, thinking her reaction was due to his weight. His hand idly stroked her waist, and he wished this moment wasn't at work, wished they were far away from everyone else.

He checked to see if she looked mad, but it wasn't anger in her eyes. It was fear. And then he heard his brother's words.

"We're ready to sell the company. Draw up the papers and have them on my father's desk by the end of the week."

Ben ground his palm against his forehead. Damn.

8

SILENTLY, HILARY GOT UP and dressed, not daring to look at Ben. She would not cry, would not cry, would not cry. She hated to cry in front of others. Crying was a sign of cupcakeness.

So why was there telltale moisture in her eyes?

Because she was a cupcake.

It didn't matter who she was, she was soon to be out of a job. Companies got bought all the time, and where there was a buyout, job cuts soon followed.

First thing when she was alone, she was calling her old boss. He'd said he would take her back if she wanted to return. And heck, it'd only been seven weeks. But she'd have to sell the house first.

What a nightmare.

She rubbed her eye and took hold of the door handle, needing to return to work.

"Hilary. Don't go yet."

Ben.

Had he known about this all along? Was this the reason he was leaving in August? She had thought she was beginning to see beneath his surface, but each time she cut a little deeper, she only ended up with more questions.

Mae wouldn't worry about such trivialities, and for Hilary, that was enough. It was safer to keep emotions in check, to keep the heart hidden away.

It took a lot of courage for her to turn and face him, and it was only after she had wiped her eyes that she did. "Yes?"

Ben had straightened his clothes and looked completely presentable, except for a hollow look on his face. Why was that? "I didn't know. I mean, I knew Dad was thinking about it, but nobody told me he'd found a buyer. I can't believe they didn't tell me."

"I'm sorry," she responded automatically.

His eyes were focused somewhere far beyond here, but then he shook his head, blinked. And voilà, there was happy, carefree Ben. Houdini. He even laughed. "Don't be. But I don't want you to worry. Promise me?"

"Ben, I worry. I angst. It's what I do. It doesn't matter if it's a leaky roof or finding ripe tomatoes at the grocery store. Equal opportunity angst is my motto."

"All right, fine. Forget that. Can you promise not to do anything rash? I'll find out more."

"Rash? Have you ever known me to do anything rash?" she answered, staring him straight in the eyes, deftly avoiding a promise she couldn't keep.

"Guess not. What about Mark? Does that mean you didn't call him? That'd be a pretty rash thing to do."

She stared, confused for a moment, then she remembered. "No. I didn't call."

He acted as if it mattered to him. "I'll pick you up at six-thirty."

"For what?"

He raised a brow. "Forgotten already?"

How could she have forgotten tango lessons? It seemed like years ago now. She clasped the door handle, trying once more. "Don't be late."

Ben grabbed her arm. "And one more thing."

"Yes?"

And he kissed her. Twice. Finally she emerged, feeling completely bewildered and a little bit drunk. "What was that for?"

"Because," he answered, completely avoiding any chance of later analysis.

"Because?" she asked, needing just a bit more to go on.

He nodded, a smile playing around his mouth. "Because."

She groaned and ripped open the door.

Men.

BEN WATCHED HER LEAVE, wanting to stay behind for just a minute. He felt for the bed, and then sat.

His dad was going to sell the company. He thought about stalking into his father's office and demanding an explanation. And what would that get him?

He could explain that he'd been thinking that maybe

he could stay on. Maybe take a position other than Security.

Ben rolled his eyes. Security.

He leaned back in the pillows, wishing he were in Colorado right now.

But no, he was in Dallas.

With Hilary.

What was he going to do with her? He tried to make himself more comfortable, but something poked him in the back. Then he reached underneath to see if he was lying on something.

The mattress was smooth, but he had definitely felt something.

He tried again, running his hands over the mattress to see if he could find where it was coming from.

Nothing.

Great, now he was imagining things.

He hadn't wanted a career in the mattress industry when he first started at MacAllister Beds, but now he was ticked that his father wasn't going to give him a chance. He hadn't wanted a relationship either, but he had a relationship with Hilary whether he planned on it or not. What the hell was he doing?

Somehow his list of things to do had changed. The ranch in Colorado was disappearing in his rearview mirror. His dreams had changed...or maybe they hadn't. Maybe these were the dreams he wanted all along and he just never knew it.

Somehow life steamrolled right over him before he'd

been able to catch his breath, before he could even blink. But the final result was an unexpected one. He'd begun to believe he was necessary—to the company, to Hilary.

But apparently that wasn't right. His dad still thought of him as security material and Hilary was itching to leave town.

Eventually he got up, determined to ignore the annoying little knot in his stomach, and the annoying big knot in the bed. He had work to do, a quarterly report to understand, and he needed to do some quick research on the tango.

BEN SHOWED UP EARLY, determined to do this right. He'd even brought her a flower. A coral rose. Not red, not yellow. Just right in the middle. Perfect.

"Ready?"

"Just a minute," she said, running off to the bathroom.

While waiting, he took a hard look at the side wall. The repairs were holding up nicely, but he really needed to put up a new truss. A small piece of white paper caught his attention. A business card. Friendly Realty. We Sell Anything.

She'd talked to a Realtor.

Then he saw the listing of Atlanta properties.

Hilary was running away. Those four words almost killed him.

Why couldn't she trust him to make things right?

Maybe she was just being smart. Got to hand it to her, she had brains.

Ben was the one who had missed the big picture. He'd thought Hilary was in for the long haul, through thick or thin. While everything else in Ben's life was changing, he thought Hilary was a constant. He must have been mistaken about that.

Softly he swore to himself and slipped the papers into his pocket. And just then she whirled into the room. He took the rose between his teeth, wiggled his brows and held out an arm. "Is madame ready to leave?"

"Of course, Antonio," she said, smiling. Happy.

He pulled open the door in true tango fashion. "Then we shall depart."

And she didn't notice when he slammed it much harder than normal.

9

THEIR DESTINATION WAS the local community college auditorium. The chairs had been pushed to the sides of the room, and there were seven other couples and the instructors—the illustrious Karen La Hoya and Charles Montero.

In Hilary's dreams, she could see herself dancing. A handsome caballero looking deeply into her eyes, their bodies pressed tightly together. The passion of the music seeping into the dance.

It was something she had never done before in her life. Yet here she was finally. Twenty-seven years old, and tonight she would dance.

She had signed up for the lessons two weeks ago, when life was rosier and full of potential. If she was leaving town, might as well leave town with a bang. Karen walked by each couple, adjusting postures and explaining the steps. She was a tall woman, with the body of a dancer, and a hand that never stayed still when she talked.

But she was certainly meticulous when it came to dance positions. Once she was finally satisfied with the arch in Hilary's back, she left them alone.

It seemed so strange to be this close to Ben, in public. Under her left hand, his arm was tense, full of power. She raised her right hand, and they matched palm to palm. Up until now, she hadn't looked at him, afraid she'd see humor in his gaze, or even worse, pity. Finally she shored up her courage and lifted her chin. However, what she saw in his eyes surprised her.

Anger.

Was he mad that they were dancing? Well, hell, that didn't make sense. He asked her to dance. What business did he have asking her if he didn't want to?

"If you don't want to be here, we can leave."

Instantly his face cleared. "No. Nowhere else I'd rather be. Let's do it."

The strains of the music began, at first slow, almost a waltz, and then the key changed and the heavy major beats sent her blood pounding.

They moved in a cat-and-mouse fashion. He stepped forward. Following his lead, she stepped back, moving on the balls of her feet. Again he stepped forward and she retreated.

It was a surprise to see the hunter in him, to see so much grace. Back and forth they moved. He pursued, she ran.

At some point, the mood intensified. She couldn't stay this close to him, listen to the smoldering sound of the violin, without her body responding.

It was as if he was making love to her. She could see it in the fire in his eyes, feel it in the heat of his touch.

Then it was her turn, and when she leaned into him, his eyes flared.

Each time they circled the floor, he drew her closer, until she knew when he breathed and her body matched the rhythms of his.

He led her around the edge of the room, faster and faster. With each press of his palm, she would turn. With each spin, they'd pull apart, and yet with one hard twist of his wrist, she would return. It was inevitable.

The music crescendoed, and for a heartbeat they would freeze. On the next hard count, he gave a sharp tug on his wrist, and she whirled into him. Slowly his hand traced her curves, and then with a final dip, the music was done.

She didn't move, caught in the web he had spun around her. He pulled her upright, his hands possessive. When he held her so tightly, she could forget everything.

It would be easy to just drown in all that heat and fire. And for tonight, she decided, she would.

BEN DROVE HER HOME after the lesson, silent. Hilary confused him and challenged him, and most of all, she could seduce him with a single look.

There were so many things to say to her, but Ben didn't want to talk. He needed to touch her.

When he parked outside her house, he started to have the discussion, but then he met her eyes. He didn't want to think about tomorrow, or about anything else. Truth was, he didn't care whether he was going to Colorado, or staying right here. The answer was much more simple. He had to kiss her.

Every guy has his own repertoire of kissing. There is the "let's have sex" thrust kiss. The more refined lips-clinging kiss which is code for "I respect you too much for the thrust kiss," and the kiss that Ben labeled "other" that fell into neither category. Somehow in his relationship with Hilary, "other" kisses were the norm. He looked forward to them, liked the way he knew exactly when her mouth changed, and she let go. He got a little thrill knowing he could make her do that.

She met him halfway on the bench seat. He took her in his arms—just one kiss was what he promised himself. One kiss lapsed into two, then more. Hilary curled into his lap, her curves fitting him perfectly. Soon the windows were fogged, his truck warm and secure. He could have stayed there all night, merely kissing her.

A car drove down the street, the headlights illuminating their safe haven. Hilary pulled away, stared at him in the dark, and then uttered those four words that spelled doom.

"I want to talk."

Ben realized that "other" kisses were done for the night, to be followed by the twelve-step program that foretold a relationship between a man and a woman. This had never been his talent. No, he could ski, could handle power tools, had recently discovered a talent for accounting, but relationships terrified him.

Once inside, he took her chair rather than the couch—this wasn't going to be a comfortable conversation—and she went to the kitchen to get wine.

A part of him knew what was coming—it was a speech he had heard before. "Where is this relationship headed?"

Ben usually responded with a question, a good technique to avoid confrontation. "Where would you like it to go? I enjoy your company and thought we could take things slowly."

While he waited for her to return, he searched his mind wanting to know how she'd answer. He didn't know where she thought their relationship was headed. Maybe at one time he had thought he did, but that was before she started looking for houses in Atlanta.

Twelve hundred miles could put a real damper on a relationship. Twelve hundred miles could put a real knife into a man's heart.

He could ask her to stay. Of course, then she'd want to know why she should. He could tell her that he intended to open his father's eyes and show him that he could take over the company.

Before he could follow that particular train of thought, she emerged with two glasses of wine. Not a bottle, which would indicate a lengthy visit, but two half-filled glasses, or two half-empty glasses, depending on your point of view.

She took the couch, had a sip of her wine, and then surprised him with the truth.

"I'm going to move back to Atlanta." The words were definitive, no question in her eyes. She didn't even ask his opinion. "I've seen what happens in takeovers, and my finances can't afford the risk. I'm sorry."

She was apologizing to him for leaving. That was a neat trick. He was being absolved of all blame in the failure of their relationship—she took that on herself.

This was the part where he asked her to stay. He opened his mouth. "I'm sorry that you feel you have to leave." Not exactly right, but a good answer nonetheless. It implied that he wanted her to stay, but that he respected her right to make up her own mind. Hilary needed her independence. She'd been hurt and wasn't in a position to take on a new challenge. Like Ben.

"I thought you'd understand," she said softly. Earlier he had heard the spark of bravado in her voice, now that spark was long gone.

"Yeah, always smart to play the odds. You'd do good in Vegas." He sipped his wine, watched as she curled her feet under her.

"I used to love to play poker with my dad." Her smile grew gentle and fond and he wished that he could make her smile like that.

"Were you any good?" he asked.

"I beat him a couple of times. My last win was April

24, 1988. My senior year in high school, right before graduation."

She wasn't the sort of girl he would have talked to in high school. She would have taken college-credit classes while he was trying to cop a feel from the head cheerleaders. "You haven't played since?"

"I used to play with Mark, but he didn't like to lose, so I would throw the games. He never caught on."

Either Mark wasn't very smart or maybe he was just intimidated by Hilary. It was odd to think that a woman with a perpetual coffee stain on her shirt could be intimidating, but Hilary could do that. She made a man wonder about his own capabilities, made a man realize his own limitations.

She leaned back on her couch, took a long sip and closed her eyes.

Already she was shutting him out. Pain wasn't an emotion that Ben usually allowed, but this pain spilled over his defenses. He gestured toward what should have been her bedroom. "You going to unpack or just leave all your boxes intact?"

"I haven't given it much thought. Work's been so busy…" She shrugged.

He hated the thought of all those boxes just sitting there, reeking of her departure. "I think you should unpack. You'll stay through the conference, right? That's another six weeks."

"Oh, yeah. I'll be around for a while. I've got to put my house on the market, and that'll take a few months.

I wanted to fix up a few things before I did that. Try to maximize my investment."

He stared into the darkness of his glass. "Glad you're going to stick around."

"What about you? Are you still going to Colorado? Big adventure."

"Might not have a choice, huh? Dad sells the company..." It was Ben's turn to shrug. He had a hard choice, facing a life of short-term adventure, or staying here long-term, trying to eke out something, when he had no idea what it was.

Hilary coughed, one of those social coughs, and he raised his head. "I still want to see you," she said, "if that's okay with you?"

Somewhere in the past twenty minutes, she'd taken the reins from him. A few weeks ago he would have been ecstatic to be in a no-strings relationship with Hilary, but now he wanted strings. Strings would keep her in Dallas. His smile was a true testament to his acting abilities. "Well, of course. It'll be my job to make sure your last few months are memorable."

"Yeah." She rubbed her temples with her forefingers and he saw the strain on her face.

"Listen, you should get some rest. I'll see you at the office tomorrow."

He leaned over and kissed her. A simple meeting of lips, no subliminal meaning at all. Then he stuck his hands in his pockets and walked out her door.

THE WEEK PASSED quietly for Hilary. Ben was there, helping her work through the plans for the conference. Polite, attentive and completely aloof. On Tuesday he came over, paintbrush in hand, and then caulked and painted her bedroom. At ten-thirty he gave her a simple kiss and left.

Not exactly what she had hoped for.

On Wednesday night, Hilary joined the illustrious Dr. Tracy MacAllister and the gracious Mary Lynn MacAllister for burgers at the Greenville Avenue Bar and Grill. At first, Hilary was in awe of Dr. Tracy, watching as a few customers approached her for an autograph.

It was Mary Lynn who finally broke the ice. "Hilary, I understand you've been having a hard time of it recently."

"I suppose, but it's turning out for the best." The Realtor had told her that the housing market was hot and she could have an offer within a few months. As soon as she sold her house, she was definitely heading back home to Atlanta.

Home seemed safer.

Mary Lynn smiled, pushing her plate out of the way. "Yes, I suppose it is. I was scared to be on my own. And now, look at me. I can howl with the best of them. I wasn't sure how the divorce would turn out."

"Oh, I didn't realize it was happening so soon."

"Just signed the papers last week," she said with a tight smile.

"That must be very difficult for you."

Tracy sipped her glass of water, never drinking deeply, only drawing tiny sips. "Marriage can be a very confining institution if one of the partners is not in the right frame of mind. Oftentimes, divorce causes an almost euphoric state of freedom, but unfortunately it's only an illusion."

Mary Lynn scrubbed at her nails with the napkin. "Stifle it, Tracy."

"I'm only stating what we all know."

Ben's mother looked up with the blue eyes that were so like his. "And what's Allen doing tonight?"

"Getting the carpets cleaned," Tracy answered.

Mary Lynn beamed. "Marvelous. It's a mother's dream to see her sons involved in the domestic arts. Allen was always the slob. Ben was always neat. Too neat."

Hilary perked up. "He was? Is?"

"Oh, my, yes. I worry about Ben."

Hilary picked up her fork and spun it on the tablecloth. "Why?"

"No mother likes to see her child in pain. It doesn't matter if he's two or twenty-nine."

"I don't think he's in pain," Hilary said. Ben didn't feel pain.

Mary Lynn tapped her forehead. "You think a mother doesn't know?"

Under the table, Hilary curled her toes until it hurt. This was the last thing she needed to hear. Ben was fine. He didn't need her. Ignoring the sharp pull on her heart, she changed the subject. "Tracy, congratulations on the new show."

"Bless you. We're over the moon. You should see Allen—he's so cute."

Trying to reconcile Allen with cuteness was difficult, but Tracy seemed enthusiastic, so Hilary smiled politely. "Oh," she said, which seemed noncommittal enough.

"Now then, who's up for Sex on the Beach?"

Hilary coughed, nearly spewing her soda. "Pardon?"

Mary Lynn summoned the waiter, a fresh-faced eighteen-year-old, who didn't look old enough to serve alcohol. "Young man, three drinks. Sex on the Beach for me. Hilary?"

Hilary cleared her throat. Maybe it was time to live a little. "Make it two."

Tracy just smiled. "You girls, go ahead. I'll stick with my water. Somebody needs to be a designated driver. All of our actions have repercussions."

Mary Lynn rolled her eyes behind Tracy's back and Hilary pretended she didn't see. After the waiter brought the drinks, Mary Lynn held up her lethal concoction. "To men."

Tracy and Hilary clinked glasses and then Hilary drank. *Yuck.*

"What made you move to Dallas, Hilary?"

She smiled, a little groggy, the fast buzz of the alcohol making her want to say *fate*. "Work."

"A new adventure?" Mary Lynn pressed.

Adventure. Did she have adventures in her life? "More like a new start."

"Sounds like there's a tale there."

"Woman. Man. Stupid mistakes. 'Nuff said."

Mary Lynn nodded wisely. "Ah."

The alcohol kicked in, and as she stared into those caring blue eyes, she wanted to cry. "Are we genetically disposed to stupidity when it comes to men?"

"Honey, you're not going to be the first, and you're certainly not going to be the last."

No, Hilary was never the last. The one before the last, the one second to the last, maybe even the one in the middle. But never the last one. She turned to Dr. Tracy, a wellspring of common sense. "Tracy, what do you think?"

"I think it's irresponsible to blame our own weaknesses on genetic tendencies. Obviously there is an anthropological pull to our sexual behaviors, but if we display foolish behavior, should we blame our DNA? I don't think so. Don't you agree?"

Hilary actually liked the idea of blaming her doormatness on something innocent—like her ancestry. But she did like Tracy. Although maybe she liked her better when she was telling an anonymous caller to get a clue, rather than Hilary.

On the other hand, that was petty. Hilary took another sip. "I think it's all fascinating."

Mary Lynn snorted. "Tracy, did you ever think to consider that perhaps love causes a bit of irrationality?"

"Spoken from the woman who just signed her divorce papers."

"I think it proves my point very nicely."

"Ladies, ladies," Hilary tried to intervene. The last thing she needed was a barroom brawl.

Mary Lynn fixed Hilary with one of those laser-beam looks. "Hilary, you've been in love, haven't you?"

Had she ever been in love? Hilary took a deep breath. "Yes, I was engaged once." Mark was Mr. Average, ten pounds overweight, but dependable, with a goofy sense of humor. Not a huge prize, which made him dumping her even more humbling.

But now it hurt less and she wondered if Mark had been love or a habit, like Monday night lasagna. She worried what that made Ben, who was not Mr. Average, a habit, nor Monday night lasagna.

"And did you behave in an irrational manner?" Again with the laser-beam eyelock and Hilary shifted in her chair.

With Mark, she hadn't had an irrational bone in her body. With Mark, she would have never attempted tango dancing, although roof repair was probably likely. Desperately she hung on to that thought.

Who was she kidding, she was doomed. The sooner she got the hell out of Dodge, the better. Ben was one hundred percent guaranteed heartbreak. Why? Because...she thought for a minute, trying to be rational with peach schnapps humming in her brain. Because if she cared too much, she was going to get hurt. Why? Because she was Hilary Sinclair, and she would always get hurt.

"I suppose I was a little irrational." It was the truth.

Mary Lynn leaned back in her chair, nodding in satisfaction.

But Tracy wasn't done. "A woman who behaves without proper self-respect will be subject to those males who prey on these poor sort of women. A man will never hesitate to use a woman for his own needs."

"Sometimes a woman's got to trust her heart. Isn't that right, Hilary?"

Hilary held up a hand. "I'm not real big on that 'trusting the heart' thing. In my experience, a heart is not a good character reference. A man needs to be judged on his actions, not on my ventricles."

Tracy began to clap. "Brava, Hilary. I couldn't have said it better. Maybe I can use that on the next show."

"But men can change," Mary Lynn interjected.

Tracy shook her head, blond curls billowing artfully. "Don't make excuses. We are always making excuses for them."

Mary Lynn sat forward. "You don't think men can change? Allen has changed."

"Well, yes, but he changed before we were married. I didn't go into our relationship expecting him to change. He'd already done all the work."

"Sometimes you have to be patient. Sit back and wait."

Wait. Yeah, she'd waited seven years. Hilary looked Mary Lynn square in the eye. "A woman can't wait forever. She'd be stupid to wait indefinitely."

"And you're not a stupid woman, are you?"

"No, ma'am." Not anymore. She'd done stupid in the past, this time she'd do smart.

BEN WAS SLOWLY going out of his mind. Each day he went through the motions of work, and each night he came home to his empty apartment and watched late-night TV until all that was left was infomercials.

It was Wednesday night, and the lady on television was lauding the virtues of her miracle stain remover, when Ben had had enough.

Things had always been easy for him—maybe they'd been too easy—but now he needed to make some changes in his way of handling things. He couldn't wait any longer, because this was a pilgrimage that was going to take some time.

The next morning Ben went on a hunt to find his father. To his surprise, his father wasn't big-game hunting or getting his pilot's license, but sitting in his big leather chair in his office, talking on the phone.

Martin MacAllister motioned for Ben to have a seat

and, for the next ten minutes, Ben listened while his father bought a horse.

Finally he hung up the phone. "I'm just about ready for Colorado."

Ben swallowed. "You're going to go?"

"Sure. Unless you got some objections. You don't, do you, boy?"

Speechless, Ben merely shook his head.

"What can I do for you? In a little early today, aren't we?"

Ben forced himself to smile. He'd been doing that a lot lately. "It's nine-thirty, Dad."

"Already? Time flies when you get to be my age."

Then Ben leaned forward, balanced his elbows on his knees and took a deep breath. Some things were harder to do. "Are you going to sell the company?"

"I think so." His father stood, his hands in his pockets and paced around the room. "Why shouldn't I take the cash and enjoy my retirement? I'm too old for the day-in, day-out grind of the mattress world. Maybe I'll go to the Galapagos. Have you been there, Ben?"

Ben waved his hand. "Yeah. Photography thing."

His dad stared him straight in the eye. "Now see, look at what you've done. And look at what I've done. I don't want to die thinking the most exciting thing I did was to ride the Shock Wave at Six Flags with my eyes closed."

"Did you really?" Ben had no idea his father liked roller coasters. Very cool.

"You're missing the point here, son. Can you blame me?" He leaned in close. "And what do you care?"

That dark gaze made Ben uncomfortable, and he got up and went to the window, staring out on the stark lines of Central Expressway. "I'm just thinking of the employees. You know, a lot of people have been with this company for more than ten years. Old Thomas Gordon in manufacturing has been here for thirteen years, Sylvia Pratt in the mailroom just celebrated her eleventh anniversary. And Debra Mordred in Human Resources was here when Grandpa ran the place."

I can do this, Dad.

Ben didn't want to turn around and face his father, see the oblivious expression on his face.

But he turned anyway. This was important to him, important to Hilary.

"There's no saying whether the new owners will dismantle the headquarters. We've been working with some boys from Japan and they'll probably keep everybody on."

At least that was something Ben could tell Hilary.

"You wouldn't do anything before the launch, right?"

"No, got too much legal mumbo jumbo to deal with." His father shook his head. "Lawyers."

Already his father was doing the paperwork. Suddenly the task seemed overwhelming, and Ben always had trouble with overwhelming.

Martin sat down in his chair and leaned back. "You got plans after Colorado?"

"Yeah," he lied.

"Too bad."

At last. Ben leaned back against the cool surface of the glass window. Not exactly executive material, but hoping to show potential. "Why?" he asked.

"Well, you know I was thinking about when we get back. I just bought myself part ownership in a race-horse, and I've a mind to visit her. Bella Donna. She's in Kentucky. How'd you like to go with me? Land of the bluegrass. Mint juleps. Hooves pounding on the turf."

Ben stood a little straighter. "Sorry, Dad."

His father shrugged. "How do you like being the Director of Security?"

Ben looked away. "Maybe I should do something else."

"Like what?"

He shrugged his shoulders. "I don't know. Something more involved in the business end or the product end."

"You don't want to do that. It's too boring for you, boy. Guaran-dill-tee-ya."

Ben met his dad's eyes but got no help there. He should just tell him, just ask. Wouldn't that be easy? But asking wasn't his style. Instead, he chose to look out the window.

Now there was something to prove—prove to his father that the wayward son had returned for good. With Hilary's help, he could do it. He didn't want to need her, but there you had it.

He looked out over all the cars on the freeway. He had never figured himself for a commuter, always pictured himself on some new adventure. However, the adventures had lost their charm.

God forbid, he was getting depth, integrity, not to mention responsibility.

He rolled his shoulders beneath all that weight. These were things he'd run from before, but now he wasn't going anywhere.

No. He was staying right here.

HILARY GOT OFF THE PHONE with her real estate agent, wishing home inspectors didn't exist. She felt good about her decision, and her parents were already counting the days.

When the doorbell rang, Hilary padded over to the door and checked the peephole. There was a truck outside her house. A big truck. The man on her front porch looked tired and sweaty.

"What is it?" she asked through the door.

"I have a delivery for this address. Are you Miss Ginger Rogers?"

"I'm sorry, that's not my name, and I didn't order anything. There must be some mistake."

"Lady, it's from MacAllister Beds."

The beginnings of a smile tugged at her mouth. Maybe it wasn't a mistake. "What is it?"

"Mattress, frame."

Hilary opened the door. "Ginger Rogers?"

"Yes, ma'am."

"All right. Bring it in."

Amazed, she stood back while the two men unloaded the mattress and then brought in the frame.

"Where do you want this thing?"

Oh, man, she still hadn't unpacked her boxes in the bedroom. Well, she could do that over the weekend. "What size?"

"King."

And why was she surprised? "I tell you what, put it over there in the corner, but just leave it in the boxes. I can put it together."

He looked taken aback. "You sure? These can be tricky."

Puh-lease. She built mattresses for a living. "I'm quite sure I can manage."

They lumbered out the door, but she remembered one last thing. "Was there any message with the delivery?"

"Yeah, but it was weird."

"What did it say?"

"Just one word. 'Because.' People sure are nutty, you know?"

10

THE NEXT MORNING, Hilary got an e-mail. "Want to go to a movie tomorrow night?"

Yes, there was nothing like a little subtlety. Deliver a bed, and then ask her out for a date. Gee. Mr. Obvious. Of course, maybe he was just being considerate. She didn't have a bed, and they *did* work for a bed company.

Nah. He wanted the sex.

And what was so bad about that? They were two consenting adults. She was going home in a few months. Under the desk, her toes scrunched tight in her serviceable pumps. If Mae could handle something like this, Hilary could, too.

She hit reply and started typing.

Ben, would love to. How about that new romantic comedy with Hugh Jackman? He's such a babe.

There. That was easy. It made her mind a little happier, but her heart still felt kind of sad.

BEN DROVE to Hilary's house right after work. He cranked up the radio, letting the deep bass shake the windows in his truck. Launch plans were proceeding nicely and although his dad hadn't yet changed his mind about selling the company, Ben thought his father was watching him. Now he just needed to make sure he didn't screw up.

And as for Hilary, she'd been watching him, too. The bed had been a masterstroke. One more way to establish Dallas as her home.

When she let him inside, he immediately noticed the king-size bed set up in the middle of her living room.

"You really didn't have to get me a bed," she said, and amazingly, she was blushing.

"You needed one."

Her head tilted to one side, looking at him suspiciously.

Immediately he was on the defensive. "Well, you did."

Finally, apparently she decided he was worthy, she nodded, prim and proper. "Thank you."

"Why didn't you set this up in the bedroom?"

Hilary shrugged. "Didn't want to deal with unpacking. This seemed easier."

Ben absorbed all that and decided that keeping her in Dallas wasn't going to be as easy as he hoped. But a man had to be prepared, and he had one more ace up his sleeve.

He bent down next to the door frame and ran his finger along the wooden trim. "Hmm..."

Instantly she was at his side. "What?"

"Well, I don't want to alarm you."

"What?"

He donned his best poker face, the one he used when he had a flush. "Did you have the house inspected for termites before you bought it?"

"Of course," she said, one foot rubbing against the other.

What was that? He looked down, and noticed her toes curling up in her sandals. "Hmm," he said, a nice ominous word.

"Why?"

He held up his finger for inspection. "Well, you see all this white powder. It's a dead giveaway."

"You don't really believe I have termites, do you?"

He waited just a beat before replying, noting the doubt in her face. "Probably not." And then he stood. He could milk the termites angle for at least another month. The real estate agent wouldn't come near it. And by then, if she was still leaving, well, he wasn't going to think about that.

HILARY ENDED UP missing most of the movie. Instead, she was hyperaware of every movement that Ben made. He brushed her arm reaching for the popcorn and instantly she froze. He whispered his own version of the ending, and instead of being angry, she melted all over her seat at the soft touch of his lips against her ear.

After the movie was over, Ben drove her home, talking about the plans for the launch. It was the conversation of co-workers, not lovers. When they arrived at her house, he left the engine running.

"Hilary..."

She lifted the door handle, ready to run. "It's all right. I can see myself in."

She opened the door and hopped out, making sure her back was perfectly straight. When she got halfway up the walk, she heard him cut the engine. When she got to the door, footsteps echoed behind her.

Pretending she hadn't heard him, she lifted her chin and turned. Slowly, so as not to appear too eager. She didn't have time to see anything, didn't have time to do anything. Without a word, he pressed her against the door and kissed her.

Why did she read so many promises in his kiss? Her arms crept around his neck and she hated her weakness.

"Stay," she whispered to him, wishing she were stronger.

"What do you need, Hilary?" he asked, his voice low and rough with need.

"I need your hands on me, your mouth. I need you inside me."

He took her chin in his hand and tilted her face until she couldn't look away. His eyes were almost grim. "That's just sex, Hilary. Is that all you need?"

Hilary leaned back against the door, not willing to lean on him. He wanted her to admit her feelings for him, give him the ultimate advantage over her. He wanted her clingy and needy, falling at his feet. Hilary had done that before, and that wasn't a mistake she was going to make again. She wanted to lie to him, keep her heart hidden far from his reach, but she couldn't lie. Still, she wouldn't give him what he wanted. "Don't make me hate you."

"Is that all you need?" he repeated.

She leaned back harder, pressing into the doorknob, welcoming the pain.

This time, she stared him straight in the eye, determined not to flinch. It made it so much more believable. "Of course."

Then she turned and opened her door and they went inside.

THIS TIME THEY'D MADE IT to the bed. Ben pulled her to him, her arms wrapping around him, just as he'd hoped. Hilary had lied. He knew it. Now he was determined to prove it to her.

Prove it to himself, as well.

She pulled at his shirt, he unzipped her skirt. He undid her bra; she tore at his fly.

He pulled her underneath him, needing to be in control, but when he sank inside her, he lost it. His whole body shuddered, and he was afraid he would come right then.

She did this to him, stripped him of all control.

She murmured his name, at first a whisper, and so he

moved harder, faster. He didn't kiss her. He wanted to watch her. See the pleasure in her eyes.

For one heart-thrilling moment, pleasure turned to need and he thrust harder, reaching deeper inside her. He took her breasts in his hands, and she bit down on her lip.

She was determined not to cry out. Determined to simply pretend that there was nothing between them. This time he wouldn't let her.

Stay. The word kept pounding in his head, until in one awful moment it slipped from his lips.

Why couldn't she see how much he needed her?

She couldn't see, caught up in fighting him. Fighting herself.

Stubborn.

Round and round they went, up and over.

Tightly his hands clenched her shoulders as he drove into her.

Even that wasn't enough. With a last deep breath, his body stiffened, and he could press no more.

"Damn it, Hilary. Trust me."

"I can't."

He took her face in his hands, willing her to understand. "I need you."

Thank God, this time she did. She leaned her forehead against his. "Stay with me," she murmured against his mouth.

This time when he moved inside her, it was as if he'd never been there before.

For a long time afterward he held her, but the wall inside her was more solid than the roof over her head.

Eventually the wall would go. It had to. Ben had climbed rocks, mountains. Hell, there wasn't a wall he couldn't scale anywhere.

Not even the one around Hilary's heart.

11

SOMETIME IN THE night she turned to him. She wanted to be tough and unbreakable, but in the cold light of day, that fantasy didn't exist. But during the night...

All things were possible during the night.

She slid a hand over his bare chest, and pressed a kiss against his neck. He sighed in his sleep, no doubt dreaming of a life that wouldn't include her.

Slowly she let her hand slide lower until she found his hard flesh. He moaned, his erection growing in her hand. In the dim light of the earliest dawn, he wouldn't notice her smile.

Her gaze trailed over broad shoulders, powerful arms, lean hips. His eyes opened and he watched her, confused, but not saying a word. She stroked him until he was fully erect, and then she slid her mouth down his chest, down his stomach, until her lips slid over his rigid flesh. Hilary licked the hard column, up, and then down, pleased when she heard him moan. Slowly she worked him over, using her mouth and tongue to pleasure him.

His hips rose, pressing him more fully into her mouth. She laid a hand over his heart, feeling his blood pump beneath her fingertips. He moved faster and she took him deeper, and it became a game. Who would give first?

Eventually she won, swallowing his fluid with ease. A woman in complete control. He pulled her up and then kissed her. "Why?" he asked.

"Complaining?" she said, meeting his lips.

"I don't understand you, Hilary, but you could kill me now and I wouldn't have enough energy to complain. What are you doing?"

"Make love to me, Ben. If you can."

He groaned, his hands touching her breasts with possessive ease. As if she mattered. He murmured her name, and she thrilled to hear the catch of desperation in his voice.

Determined to push him over the edge, she rose above him, arching her back. This time the advantage would be hers. Quietly they made love. His hands stroked her breasts, knowing exactly how she wanted to be touched. For an eternity she rode him, letting her body rule her mind.

This was about pleasure. Her pleasure. Nothing more.

Never anything more.

She felt tears building in the corner of her eye, and she moved harder, until the pressure inside her blocked out everything else.

Finally, her body was done and she collapsed on him, wishing he would promise the world. The sad irony was that if he did, she wouldn't believe him. Why would he ever fall in love with a woman like her?

He held her close, stroking her bare back, and she was glad that he held his tongue. Sometimes the words got in the way.

Hilary listened to the beat of his heart, thumping powerfully for her. She kept her own heart hidden far away. Maybe she was getting the hang of this after all.

AT FOUR-THIRTY, Hilary awoke to the sound of Ben's watch beeping. During the night, they'd moved from one position to another, and now she rummaged through the covers that he'd stolen from her.

"Gotta go."

She propped herself on one elbow and watched as he got himself dressed. "Go where?"

"I set up a breakfast meeting at seven. I need to take a look at that bed. There's a problem." He buckled his belt, gave her a quick kiss and was gone.

What problem? Leaving Hilary alone in her brand-new MacAllister bed was the only problem she could see.

She jerked the covers up over her face, determined to go back to sleep. She was not going to get upset about this, was not, was not, was not.

THREE DAYS LATER, Ben was no closer to finding any answers. He'd talked to manufacturing, talked to the engineers, but he'd avoided the one person he should be asking for help.

Now he just needed to find the misaligned spring, save the day, and have his father realize that he needed Ben to run the company.

Sure, that was doable.

And the first thing to tackle was finding the problem, so what's a guy to do?

He went to Hilary's office and knocked. Her face brightened and suddenly things looked a little less hopeless.

"I need your help. I'm not going crazy. There's a problem with the bed. It's the same thing I felt the first time I lay down on it."

"Problem with the Dreamscape line? I haven't felt anything."

"It's there. I know it is. Will you help?"

"Let's go look," she said.

They walked to the research center, and he explained what he knew, which wasn't much. "I think I know where the problem is."

"Where?"

Ben laid his hand over the mattress, felt the right side. Unfortunately it felt fine now. "Right here."

Hilary pressed down, testing the give of the bed. "And?"

It would be so easy to stop now, pretend he'd never felt anything. No, he could do this. "I've been reading about this for the past few days. I think a spring is mis-aligned. Let me get something to cut through this."

"Cut?" she echoed.

He didn't reply, but instead went to retrieve a small handsaw.

He returned, remembering his seventh-grade biology classes. "Now, look, if we rip this open here..."

He dissected the bed, as if it were a frog. Hilary watched him, looking a little pale. "Uh, we don't really need to tear that up, do we?"

It had to be here. "Yes, you've got to see this. If you look under here—" he lifted the quilted batting aside "—voilà!"

Perfectly aligned springs.

She looked up at him, her smile a little forced. "Voilà?"

He ran his hand through his hair, wondering what he'd done wrong. Maybe it was farther to the left. He bent down, eye level, but everything looked perfect. "I was sure that was it. Hil, do you see anything?"

Hilary studied the springs, the layout, and ran her hand down the line of the mattress. She even lay down on the bed, but finally she threw up her hands.

"I don't know, Ben. It feels fine to me. It looks fine to me."

He sat down, staring at the remains of the bed, rubbing his temple. "I don't understand."

She sat down next to him, her eyes soft, gentle. "Do

you think your father won't be able to sell if there's a problem? Is that what this is about?"

She thought he was making it up. Out of all people, she should believe him. "Damn it, Hilary. This isn't my imagination."

She tried to smile. "Of course it's not."

Ben stood and stuffed his hands in his pockets. "You know, my life would be much easier if people would actually have faith in me."

She didn't say anything. She didn't have to.

That was all he could take.

MARTIN MACALLISTER HELD his annual Fourth of July barbecue party at White Rock Lake. By the time Hilary arrived, there were fifty people, all ages, all walks of life. She recognized some people from work, Helga in party attire, Susan was there with a cast on her leg and two crutches, and Allen and Tracy were over by the grill.

She had expected Ben to be there. Had hoped he'd be there. Okay, that was a little needy, but it was a holiday.

They didn't have unspoken holiday-date agreements, actually not even spoken holiday-date agreements, but he had been spending several nights a week at her house.

She'd bought him his own toothbrush, which he accepted with a raised eyebrow and a memorable hour on the kitchen table. He kept a spare set of clothes there now—just to have something clean to change into when they were done with home repairs.

On most days, she was quite rational, not letting herself worry about the uncertain drift in their relationship. But about every fifth day, she hit a slump and freaked herself out.

It would be much easier if he confessed his undying love or begged her to move in with him or even better yet—whisked her off to elope.

None of which meant she was in love.

Sometimes being a woman sucked.

Hilary took a sip of her venti decaf latte and pretended she wasn't waiting for him.

Finally she took out her cell phone and called Home Depot to check and see if the new windows were in. And if the clerk thought it was strange that she wouldn't let him off the phone for fifteen minutes, he handled it nicely.

Just last week, Ben had taken apart the wood floor in her living room and replaced it with Pergo, which looked very nice and chichi. The termites were still an issue, and Ben thought her pipes were rusting out and would need to be replaced before she could sell. Another five grand that she couldn't afford.

She wanted to be back in Atlanta soon, but every time Ben found a new problem with her house, it seemed to delay her leaving a little more.

When she looked over, Martin MacAllister himself

was handing out plates of ribs and potato salad. Enough angst—time to eat.

"Hilary, how you doing this evening?"

"Fine, thank you, Mr. MacAllister."

"Here, take some sauce. It'll burn your socks off, but it's good."

"Ben says you're buying a racehorse. I saw the derby one time when I was eight. Wow. Good luck."

"He said I was buying a horse? Not in this lifetime."

"No, that's what he said. I don't think he misunderstood. And the motorcycle, the Winnebago...have you been feeling well, Mr. MacAllister?"

He piled some potato salad on her plate, one, two, three spoonfuls. "Been feeling fine. As a matter of fact, never felt better."

"There is no racehorse?"

"Nope."

"The Winnebago?"

"Maybe, but probably not."

"Why are you doing this to Ben?"

"It takes Ben some time to make up his mind about things. I'm just testing to see what he wants." Then he winked. Such a simple, conspiratorial gesture.

"I guess I misunderstood," she murmured.

"Maybe, maybe. Big plans tonight?"

"I thought I'd go over to Mary Lynn's later."

"You tell her I said hello."

"Will do."

"You going to see my son tonight?"

She had prayed so hard that she would. A holiday-date, that meant something. Even the Fourth. But he knew her plans, and here she was alone. "I don't know, sir. I thought he'd be here."

A shadow crossed his face. "I thought he would, too. It'll be the first MacAllister barbecue he's ever missed."

Hilary talked with Tracy and Allen for a while, traded recipes for Jell-O salad with Helen Sharpe from finance, and spent another fifteen minutes talking to the time and temperature recording.

After an eternally long half hour, she realized that Ben wasn't going to show. After finishing her food and offering goodbyes, she hopped into her car and went to party number two.

Mary Lynn MacAllister lived in a small apartment in a northern suburb of Dallas, a tidy community with tall gates and, according to the signs, four pools and free cable.

Ben's mother opened the door. "Hilary, what a nice surprise. I was hoping you would come. Except I think most of the guests are a little bit more mature than you'd prefer."

"I just stopped by to say hello."

"Since Ben wasn't here, I figured you and he might have some plans tonight."

"No, ma'am."

Mary Lynn shook her head. "That boy. If he wasn't my own flesh and blood...I had high hopes for the both of you."

High hopes. Hilary didn't believe in high hopes. She smiled politely. "We're at different places in our lives."

"If that's what you think, suit yourself. Well, I can't ignore my guests. Make yourself at home."

"Listen, I'm getting a little tired. I just wanted to stop by. By the way, Mr. MacAllister said to tell you hello."

She emitted a long sigh. "Sometimes I sure miss him."

"Have a happy Fourth."

"You, too, Hilary."

WHEN SHE GOT HOME, she discovered exactly where Ben had been. Mowing her lawn. He was dressed in old shorts and a T-shirt that had seen better days. Her porch railing had been painted, too.

My, my, someone has been busy.

As she got out of her car, she signaled for him to shut the engine off.

"You've been working."

"Yeah, needed to get some of this done."

"By the light of the moon?"

The telltale bottle rocket popped overhead.

"The streetlights are pretty bright."

"Why don't you come inside? It looks like you could use something to drink."

He wiped the sweat from his forehead. "Nah. I'll just finish up."

Okay, maybe she loved him. She was a sucker for a man who did lawn maintenance. When he was like this, so helpless and vulnerable, she could believe that he would never hurt her. She smiled. "You know, I could use a new door, too."

He checked his watch. "There's a twenty-four-hour Home Depot up north. I could take care of it tonight if you want."

"That was a joke, Ben."

"Oh, yeah."

Usually he caught on faster than that, but he was wiped. She tugged on his arm. "Come inside."

He tugged back. "I really need to finish this up."

"I went to your dad's barbecue. And your mom's margarita party. They both asked about you."

"Okay." He pulled at the lawn mower, the loud engine drowning out any chance of conversation.

She shut it off.

He took hold of the pull string. "I really need to finish this."

"No."

He stood back. "What is it, Hilary?"

"You can't hide from your parents' situation. This isn't healthy."

"You've been spending too much time listening to Tracy. Not everyone needs to be psychoanalyzed."

His eyes held so much pain that she wanted to cry for him, shed all the tears he couldn't. "It's almost nine o'clock."

"So?"

"Come inside. Talk to me."

"Words are useless. Words never fix anything. They sure as hell aren't going to fix this. So, rather than sitting around feeling sorry for myself, I should do something constructive. Like mow your lawn. Now if you'll excuse me."

She put her hands on her hips. It was time to get tough. "I'll call the cops. Tell them that some strange man is out mowing my lawn."

Finally he caved. "You would, wouldn't you?"

"Damn straight. Put that thing away and come inside. You have a lawn mower? I thought you lived in an apartment." An apartment she'd never been to, she thought to herself.

"Took it from Allen's house. He'll never notice. I need to borrow your shower."

"I insist."

"Rank?"

"Manly," she said, liking the smile she brought to his face.

"YOU SMELL LIKE MANGOS."

He pulled a face. "Disgusting, isn't it?"

"I think it's sweet."

"See? What happened to manly? I like manly."

It seemed wiser to change the subject, so she said, "You want to watch the fireworks on TV?"

"Got a better idea," he said, pulling her hand and walking outside. "Where's your ladder?"

"In the shed out back."

"Wait right here."

He returned a minute later and set up the ladder against the side of the house. "You first."

"Up on the roof?"

"Yeah, it'll be great."

"What if my roof falls in?"

"We don't weigh that much."

"Rain doesn't weigh much, either."

"Come on, climb up. The fireworks are just starting."

"If I fall, I'm suing your ass."

She climbed up on the roof, hanging on for dear life.

He scrambled up behind her, then started walking around. *Walking around.* As if they were on the ground or something.

"Show-off," she muttered, making sure he heard her.

"Stand up."

"No, thank you. I've very comfortable here."

"Trust me. Give me your hand. I promise you won't fall." He looked over the edge. "Besides, it's only ten feet to the ground."

Hilary took hold of his hand and he pulled her upright. "See, that's not so bad. Look around you. You're on top of the world."

She stared out onto the towering oaks and concrete streets. "It's not Paris."

"You gotta start somewhere, Hilary. Might as well be Dallas."

She moved a foot, testing whether she would fall. "Okay, this isn't awful."

He pulled her into his arms and then, jerk that he was, he dipped her. Ten feet off the ground, on a roof that wasn't designed for dancing.

But then it was over. She was a little light-headed, her heart was pounding a bit much, but she did it.

Wisely she sat. He sat down next to her and then leaned back against the roof. "Best place to watch fireworks."

"You do this a lot?"

"First time."

Slowly she leaned back, careful not to look out over the edge. "Sorry about your mom and dad."

"It happens."

She took his hand and didn't say anything more. Instead, they watched the sky light up with color, oohing and aahing at the appropriate places. When the sky turned dark, and the show was over, they climbed back down to earth.

"I SHOULD GO."

"You could stay."

He nodded. "Yeah, I could."

This time when they made love, the usual concerns were forgotten. Tonight the world was soft and slow, a place of peace. Before, he had said he needed her, but tonight was the first time that she felt that he truly did.

BEN WOKE EARLY. Three days before the conference in Vegas. Three days to figure out what was wrong with the bed. He went to the research center and studied the springs, but he didn't understand this stuff.

Everything looked right to him.

His dad found him there, just sitting on the floor, staring at the exposed mattress.

"Morning, Ben. Practicing your anger management?"

"I know there's a problem with the bed."

His dad scratched his head. "Don't think so. We don't make beds with problems."

"Yeah, there is. I just don't know what it is."

"You talked to Pat, the production foreman?"

Ben nodded. "He just stared at me like I was crazy. Maybe I am crazy."

"Well, you didn't get it from me, that's for sure. You've been doing a great job. Never seen you apply yourself like this before. It makes a father proud."

Ben looked up at his father, studying the dark eyes that never gave anything away. "You signed the paperwork yet?"

"For what, the ranch in Colorado?"

"No, the company."

"Ah, that. No, been too busy. Thought I could sign in Vegas. Yamamuro-san will be there."

"Too bad."

"Got something to say, son?"

"Nah, just want to find this problem."

"Well, keep looking. I think I'm going to go sailing today. Nothing like being on the water, is there?"

"Have fun, Dad."

"You, too."

THAT AFTERNOON, he brought Steve over to take a look. Steve was the best engineer he knew, although his specialty was construction, not beds.

"What do you think?"

Steve wandered around the bed, pushing here and there. "I don't know, Ben. It looks sound to me."

"I can't believe this." Ben climbed on to the mattress and lay down. "I can feel it." He felt behind him. "It's right here." He started to get up, but Steve pushed him back.

"No, wait. Stay there." Steve bent down and studied the springs at eye level. "I think I see it. When there's no weight on the bed, it's level, but after you put your full weight down, the spring doesn't fully compress."

"Really? Why that one?"

"Don't know. Let's see." Steve took out a screwdriver and began to pry out the springs. "Yup. And there it is."

Ben looked down in the well of the bed. "What?"

"See that rivet under there?"

"Yeah."

"It's preventing the coil from contracting completely."

"And that's it?"

"Think so."

"Manufacturing should have found this earlier."

Steve laughed. "You'd be surprised how many times this happens in a new design. Mattresses, cars, computers. Mass production is not an exact science. But you'll figure that out soon enough. You going to stay?"

"Yeah."

"You've changed, Ben."

"Some."

"We'll be glad to have you around. I found some great fishing up at Grapevine."

"Fishing sounds good. Steve, my man, I owe you a beer."

Steve rubbed his chin. "Nah, I'm thinking dinner. Morton's."

The world was a fine place. "You got yourself a deal."

BEN FOUND HIS FATHER in his office, Hilary sitting across the desk from him, all sorts of papers in between the two. Talking business. Without him.

He supposed that was okay, but only because while they were discussing distribution schedules, he was out fixing the product line.

"I found it. It was a misaligned spring."

Hilary turned and looked, those intelligent green eyes more thoughtful than Ben would have liked.

His father started to grin. "Well, I'll be. And here I thought you were full of it."

"No, Dad," Ben said, and then fully explained what he found.

Martin MacAllister reached into his desk and pulled out a wine bottle. "You need to talk to manufacturing, make sure they fix the units we're shipping out there. I can't believe it. Well, this calls for a celebration. A problem with the Dreamscape could've ruined the deal. Needed a reason to break out this bottle of saki from Yamamuro-san. Anybody?"

Ben felt for the chair behind him, his hand gripping the hard wood as tight as he could. Impossible. "You're still going to sell the company?"

"Well, sure. Why shouldn't I?"

Ben felt a sharp poke in the side. Hilary's gaze shifted to his father meaningfully. Ben shook his head. His father had to realize this.

He wouldn't beg, wouldn't ask for something his father didn't think he deserved.

But that didn't mean that Ben couldn't throw out strong hints. "You can't think of any reason at all?"

His father simply shook his head. "Nope. What about China? See the Great Wall. Wouldn't that be a hoot? You want to come with me?"

Ben stalked out of the room, his father's booming laughter echoing down the hallway.

What did a man have to do to get noticed around here anyway?

HILARY DIDN'T TAKE long to dig into him. She waited as far as his office and then closed the door. "Why didn't you just ask?"

"No."

"Why not?"

"Because I want to earn it, Hilary. I don't want it given to me."

She flashed him her patented eye roll. "This is real life, Ben, not a made-for-television movie. What about all those people depending on you? Is your pride more important?"

"This isn't about pride."

"What is it about, Ben?" she asked, her voice softening.

This time the answer was easy. "He needs me. I can do this, and I want him to see that. If I ask, I might as well be roping cows in Colorado."

VEGAS WAS THE CITY of lights, and nowhere in the world could compare. This week it was home to the International Sleep Products Expo, an industry that prided itself on everyone getting a good night's sleep, but that was an impossibility in Vegas.

The show was full of mattresses, materials and bed frames all lined up, row after row, as far as the eye could see. Ben wandered through the aisles, first as a novice, but then as a professional.

He had learned a lot, but still had much left to master. The mattress industry wasn't the walk in the park he had always assumed it was. He should have given his father and Allen more credit.

And Hilary, as well.

His list of "things to do before I die" was quickly changing. He'd scratched everything else off, and added two new things and when they got back to Dallas, he'd start working on item number two. Right now there was item number one to worry about.

Overall, the launch went without a hitch and after the show, Mr. MacAllister threw a party to end all parties at his suite. Hilary was the first thing Ben saw, decked out in a dark gray business suit that clung tightly, showing off her curves to all the world. Her hair was perfectly smooth, glistening in the light. And when she smiled, men turned their heads.

This confident, elegant woman was not his Hilary, and he wanted to take her away. He wanted the prickly, bristling woman who pushed him forward, made him think he could do anything. He had started to walk toward her with every intention of getting her alone, when his father snagged him.

"Ben, wonderful job. Couldn't have done it without you."

"Thanks, Dad."

"And now let me introduce you to Toshi Yamamuro, president of FujiYama Enterprises."

Ben bowed to the distinguished Japanese gentleman and greeted him in the traditional manner.

Mr. Yamamuro bowed. "It is an honor to meet you, Mr. MacAllister. Your father has told me great things about you."

Ben's gaze slid to his father, wondering.

"And now to have this opportunity to own his product line…"

"Dad, can we talk for a minute?"

His father clapped an arm around his shoulder. "Surely it can wait until we finish this little ceremony."

"No, it can't."

Martin turned to Yamamuro. "*Sumi masen*, Yamamuro-san, my son seems to have something up his sleeve. Wants to go off and be a race-car driver, I bet," he said with a laugh.

At no time in his life had Ben *ever* wanted to be a race-car driver, and he wasn't in the mood for jokes.

Enough was enough. Ben pulled his father off to a corner to talk; this time he didn't waste words. "Dad, I want to run the company."

His father looked surprised. "Which company?"

"MacAllister Beds."

"Oh. I always thought it wasn't your cup of tea."

"I was wrong."

"Hmm…"

"You can't sell the company."

"If you were running it, how would you do it? You must have some ideas."

"I think we can increase the distributorship by fifteen percent in the United States, and I think there's a significant market in Europe that we could tap into with the right channels."

"You think you could do all that?"

"I can try."

"Son, I've been wanting to sell the company, take the proceeds and do some real living. Now you're telling me you want to run it. If so, what will my take be?"

"You can keep the same percentage of the profits you keep now. You could keep your salary, too, if you want. I'm not after the money, Dad."

"You know how much profit we made last year?"

"Yes."

"Well, it's not going to get me to the Galapagos."

"It's not called MacAllister Beds for nothing. I'm a MacAllister. I can do this."

"I don't know. It takes determination, skill, responsibility."

"Hilary will help me."

"Maybe we should ask her about that." Martin waved at Hilary and she walked over to them. She didn't realize she held his future in her hands, but there was no one that he trusted more.

"Got a question for you, ma'am," his father asked.

"Yes, sir."

"My son is talking me into letting him run Mac-Allister Beds, and he thinks he's qualified. What do you think?"

Hilary gave Ben a long, considering look. "I think he's brighter than you give him credit for, more determined than most people would guess, and personally I think he's capable of tremendous things."

She really thought all that? Ben began to smile, and it

had nothing to do with MacAllister Beds and everything to do with Hilary.

"He's not very experienced," his father added.

"No, sir. Not in the sleep products industry."

Now that little remark would require payback, and he began to contemplate all the glorious types of payback he could administer.

"He said that you would help him with the company. That's a big job. Is that something you would agree to?"

"He needs my help?" She stared at Ben. Something vague brewing in her green eyes made him nervous and uncertain. "If he needs me, of course I'd be there, but I don't think I'm critical to the running of MacAllister Beds when Ben's at the helm. You're selling him short, sir." Then she looked away. "Selling him short would be a mistake."

HILARY WAITED for Ben in her room. Martin MacAllister had gone all out for everyone, and she had a suite that rivaled Versailles. The ceiling was painted with cavorting angels, and antiques were scattered through the room in a deceptively languid manner.

In the center of the room sat a four-poster bed with carved posts that reached to the ceiling. It was the absolute greatest bed she'd ever seen in her entire life, and she might as well enjoy the one night she had.

Ben had what he wanted. He was going to run

MacAllister Beds. Testing out his wings, proving himself to the world.

He would do fine.

After all, he had finally found everything he needed.

She was troubled because, in his success, she could realize her own failure. Seven years she had waited for Mark, waited in a contented fog. How long would she wait for Ben? He was the kind of guy you waited a lifetime for. For him, she would do it. That was a scary thought, so this time she was going to be smart.

She took off her makeup and shook out her hair, staring at the plain girl who stared back at her. Cinderella she wasn't. No, she more closely resembled the older stepsister, the hard-hearted one.

Midnight came and went, and at half past one, he knocked.

Ben was beaming, glowing, dancing on the ceiling. At least somebody was having a good time. He brought out a bottle of champagne and she pasted on a smile.

"I couldn't have gotten here without you."

And that kind of talk she wouldn't tolerate. "Yes, you could. It just would have taken longer."

He kissed her, long and lingering. A typical Ben MacAllister kiss that never failed to set her on fire. He popped the cork on the bottle and poured two glasses.

She raised her glass. "To the new head of MacAllister Beds."

"Thank you." He took a long swallow. "So what do

you think I should tackle first? The European market or domestic front?''

She hid her wince from him. "Can we not talk business?''

Smiling, he arched a brow. "Got some other ideas?''

She drew a finger over the rim of the glass. Very Mae. Since she'd met him, she'd acted out her fantasies, and there were a few more still left to live. "Yeah, I do.''

He snapped his fingers. "Wait a minute.'' After fishing around in his pockets, he brought out a deck of cards, complete with the hotel logo. "I believe madam has mentioned poker before?''

Why had she told him that? Why had she bared her soul to the man least likely to notice? But he had noticed. Once again, she'd sold him short. "Oh, no.''

His smile turned wicked and he raised a brow. "Chicken?''

Like hell. She sat down on the small sofa and cracked her knuckles. "Straight poker. Jokers are wild.''

He sat down next to her and shuffled the cards like a pro. As he dealt the cards, smooth and fast, she had the sneaking suspicion she was being hustled. No matter, she could hold her own. Hilary had learned long ago, she could always hold her own.

His hand had a two showing and she peeked at her own cards. A pair of fours and little potential for anything else.

"I'll bet one shoe.''

"That bad, huh? I'll raise you another shoe and one tie."

She discarded three cards and picked up trash. Sadly she shook her head. "Fold."

He had two pairs. He raised his brows and she made a nice show of kicking off her shoes and removing her handkerchief.

Next hand, she had equally bad luck. She lost her hose and a half-slip. After she lost her skirt, Ben took her hand. "Hilary honey, as much I should shoot myself for saying this, I know for a fact you can play with more imagination. Are you trying to throw this game just because you want to get naked for me?"

She scowled at him. "You egotistical clod. I'll show you what I can do."

And lo and behold, the next hand she bluffed him out of his shoes and tie. Yeah, take that, Buckeroo. Of course, the next hand he won her skirt, but then she got his jacket and shirt.

When he took off his shirt, she did ogle him, but only for a minute, and only when he wasn't looking. The man was muscular and tanned, nice balance of chest hair and skin, and if he had a physical flaw, it wasn't apparent. And she had looked for it, too.

The next hand, simply because she was distracted, she lost her blouse. At least she could be grateful that she wore her lacy bra tonight. Always wear your good underwear just in case you get conned into a game of strip poker. Not her mother's advice, but sage wisdom nonetheless.

Hilary won Ben's trousers and belt on an inside straight, but still he wore that confident grin. "Bet you're thinking you got me right where you want, Miss Hilary Sinclair. But I'm thinking that bra is mine."

"Tough words from a man wearing only his Hanes."

"Getting a little anxious?"

She pulled one of her bra straps off her shoulder, letting it fall, and she was delighted to note his eyes heated to liquid blue. "Not at all."

Sadly enough, he won her bra with only a pair of jacks.

Slowly she took it off, and he sighed effusively.

It was all silliness, but for tonight she would believe it.

The last hand was a bitter battle—bikinis or briefs. Hilary held three kings and knew she had him. He was bluffing, rubbing his chin, and eyeing her with consideration before each bet.

Finally he called. With a flourish, she laid down her three kings, and he frowned. "Damn. I can't believe it." He put down his hand and shook his head. "I don't know what I'm complaining about. You're fixing to lose yours anyway."

He pushed her back against the couch and started to pull off her panties, but she put a hand against his chest. "Uh-uh-uh."

"You are such a stickler for rules."

"Only when I win."

He began to pull off his briefs, but she stopped him. "Allow me."

Each inch of the way, she touched him and it was pure satisfaction to see the muscle working in his jaw. A true Mae moment. Finally she threw the material aside and touched the long length of him.

"That's enough. It's your turn."

And he tortured her equally well, his hands following the inside of her thigh, the back of her knee, spots that she didn't even know existed.

Oh.

He gently eased her back and spread her thighs, his fingers tracing inside her. She memorized the intent look in his eyes, the way he looked at her with such desire. Tonight would last her for years to come. Not every woman had her fantasy come to life for her.

He took his glass of champagne and poured the bubbling liquid over her breast, the cold chilling her skin, and she started to yelp, but this time she held her tongue.

As he began to trace the path of the bubbles with his mouth, she decided she would thank him. He kissed away the chills from her flesh, pulling one nipple into his mouth and sucking with a strong, low rhythm that pulsed between her legs. She rocked her hips against him, feeling his erection pressing against her. She tried to angle him closer, but he pulled back from her and shook his head.

"Not yet."

He took the bottle of champagne and poured it over her stomach, letting the cool liquid drizzle between her thighs. Then he performed exquisite tongue torture, licking her skin until she was twisting beneath him, needing him to ease the pressure building. But he grasped her hips tightly.

"No."

He nuzzled the flesh below her belly button, and sucked mercilessly. She felt only a boneless melting inside her. His mouth moved lower, his tongue tracing a path between her lips, slow, sure, the bubbles a foreign sensation amidst the whirls of pleasure that he created. She rolled her head back against the couch, too helpless to fight, and she simply let him seduce her.

There were tears in her eyes, her release threatening, and each time he took a long stroke, she climbed higher.

"Don't fight me, Hilary. Go with it."

And she did. Though Hilary had the sense that she'd always been destined to lose.

THE MORNING SUN WAS just starting to come up, poking through the curtains, casting its warming rays on the tangle of sheets. Morning. A new day. Hilary closed her eyes, wanting to see if the doubts would come and hoping that they wouldn't. So far, so good. But then she had to open her eyes, because she couldn't keep them closed forever, and she stared at his sleeping face, the taut perfection of his body.

She stared directly into the cold light of day and all the doubts came roaring, screaming into her mind. Big, in red flashing letters that even the blindest woman in love couldn't miss.

Tenderly, she touched his face, traced the high cheekbones, the strong nose, and then she brushed the hair out of his eyes.

The blue eyes flickered open, dark lashes shuttering his gaze, and then he smiled at her.

It was a smile that could stop her heart.

"Morning," he said.

It was time. Hilary broached the one topic that she dreaded most. "You're going to get real busy, real soon."

He leaned up on one elbow, foolishly excited. "Yeah. Do you really think I can do this?"

She had no doubts at all. The Ben MacAllisters of the world could do anything when they put their mind to it. "Of course you can."

Then he took her hand. "But you *are* going to help, aren't you? I meant what I said. I don't know what I would do without you."

Did he truly believe that? Wonder how he'd get along without her? He'd do fine. She'd do fine. Each one of them would go their separate ways, no messy breakups, no embarrassing moments when things don't work out. Life would be much simpler, much less painful. "You don't need my help. Trust me."

Oh, but he knew what she was doing. His gaze trapped her. "But you'll be there every day, under my nose, giving me advice whether I want it or not. I mean, it is your job, and you're not going anywhere, right?"

She remained stubbornly silent, wishing he would be quiet, wishing he would just leave her alone, so that she could go back home and discover that her life wasn't over.

"Hilary? Your job is secure. There's absolutely no reason to go back to Atlanta."

"My old boss offered me my job back, and I told him I'd take it."

He sat up, completely awake and more than a little formidable. "No."

But she would show no fear. "I beg your pardon?"

"I won't let you quit."

Why couldn't he understand? She just couldn't do this again. Couldn't take the pain, the sympathetic looks from her friends. Ben didn't get sympathy looks. Only a slap on the back from his buddies, telling him he'll be back in the saddle again in no time, and then they'd fix him up with their sister's best friend and he'd be in another relationship in two-point-seven days. "You don't have a choice," Hilary stated, trying to get him to understand.

"Why? Is this about your job or about me?"

She paused. "A little bit of both. You don't need me to do your job, and I think until you go it alone, you'll never know."

"That's a load of crap. It takes more than one person to run a company. You're good at what you do, Hilary. Get to the real reason."

She pulled the sheet around her and got up from the bed. She couldn't be this close to him. Distance was the key. Time he realized who she really was. "Okay, maybe it's a lot having to do with you, with me, with—this. Every day I wake up thinking, is this the day he's going to dump me? I'm not going to go through that hell again. Every morning, it's the same mantra, over and over. I don't trust you, and it has absolutely nothing to do with you."

In his eyes was the complete confusion of a man who'd never been dumped in his entire life. She hated him for that.

"And you've worked this out all by yourself?" he asked.

She went to the window and looked out over the faux Paris. In the bright light of morning, the Eiffel Tower stood all alone. "Well, it took some time before I stopped blaming you for it. You should be happy about that."

"And that's the end of the discussion, huh?"

"No, feel free to add whatever you want."

"But it won't make a damn bit of difference, will it? You're still going to run."

Hilary turned and shrugged, but there was no reason to lie. It was a liberating feeling, letting him see through the facade to all the festering nooks and crannies that plagued her. It was time he saw the real Hilary. "Probably, yes."

He got up and pulled on his pants, then shrugged into his shirt. Barefoot, he walked to the door. "You are such a piece of work. I thought there was something between us, Hilary."

She remembered the anger, the denial, and then later the guilt. He wouldn't have the guilt, but for a dark moment she wanted him to. "Yeah, you'd like that, wouldn't you? The thought that I couldn't manage my life on my own."

But embarrassingly enough, he didn't look guilty. He looked serious and hurt, and Hilary simply felt petty.

"That wasn't a joke, Hilary. It wasn't meant to be a put-down or an ego boost. It was a mere statement of fact. I thought you needed me like I need you, but if you're heading back home, then obviously I was wrong."

He swung the door open and then turned back around. "Last night? Poker? I had a full house. Three nines, and a pair of aces. You lost, Hilary." And with that he was gone.

On Monday morning, Ben was back at work. The next president of MacAllister Beds. Yee-haw. He should feel proud of what he'd done, happy even, but instead he felt empty.

He noticed that Hilary hadn't shown up yet. Not a huge surprise, but he was disappointed nonetheless.

His father had arranged for Ben to be moved to his father's old office, and so today Ben had the marvelously enjoyable task of cleaning out his desk.

He looked at the network security book, almost trashed it, but decided to keep it. After all, he never knew when he might need it again. And there in the back of the drawer he found the folder that contained all his information on the J&D ranch in Colorado.

With a tired sigh, he sat down in his chair and thumbed through the pictures of the mountains, the clouds of dust billowing under the horse's hooves, and realized the appeal wasn't there. Sure, it'd be nice to visit, but he didn't want to work there after all.

The last page in the folder was his list of "things to do before I die."

There, in black ink was the list he'd made when he was fourteen, and the two recently added additions.

Run MacAllister Beds.

Marry Hilary.

He pulled out his pen, ready to check off the first one. Been there, going to do that for the rest of his life.

And the second? He had started to cross that one off when his father knocked on the open door.

"Come on in. Just cleaning out a few things."

His dad picked up his security book, turned to the

list of chapters, and grinned. "You always were stubborn."

"Gee, thanks, Dad."

Then his father settled himself in the chair across from Ben. "That doesn't mean I'm not proud of you. You did good."

Ben smiled, locked his hands behind his head. "Yeah, I did, didn't I?"

"What's next?"

He thought for a minute, his mind wandering through the options he'd already laid out. "The European market, definitely."

"You know, if you need help finding a distributor in France or Germany or Switzerland, I could make a few suggestions. I've got some contacts in the industry."

Suspicious, Ben studied his father. "I thought you were going to Colorado?"

His dad widened his eyes, looking all innocence. "Well, sure I am. I'm talking about when I get back."

"Oh."

"You need any help, you just holler and I'll be right here."

"Thanks, Dad."

His father got up to leave, and Ben watched him walk out the door.

He stared at the list in his hand and crumpled it up into a ball. He didn't need the list anymore. He had direction in his life.

He was needed. Some comfort though when it was the job that had called to him and not Hilary.

He softly swore to himself. He should have known better than to fall for a woman with her scars. Maybe he wasn't really in love with her? Maybe it was all a fluke?

He knew that every day he couldn't wait to see her again, thought of things he needed to tell her, loved making love to her, and had pretty well dragged his dignity through the mud for her, but was that love?

Either that, or he was the world's biggest sap.

Not a comforting thought.

One thing he'd learned was that you had to fight for what you wanted. Believe in it one hundred percent. Was she worth fighting for? Worth dragging his dignity through the mud one more time? Although Hilary might argue with him—she always argued with him— he would drag his dignity through the mud a gazillion more times if she would just realize she loved him.

If Miss Contrary Sinclair thought he was going to sit quietly by while she made the biggest mistake of both their lives, she was wrong.

He pushed back from the desk and sucked in a deep breath of air. His heart was twisted into knots he couldn't begin to untie. Never had he been more uncertain, more unsure of his future.

This was truly living.

"Helga, hold my calls. I'm going out."

"You've only just got here."

He didn't know if men flirted with Helga, but it was high time that someone did. So he winked at her, enjoying the shock that came to her face. "With any luck, it'll be tomorrow before I come back."

HILARY WAS intimately familiar with the differing levels of guilt that came with being a woman. The first level, the easy level was reserved for mild-mannered offenses, being a day late on her electric bill, scarfing a cookie in the grocery store and forgetting to pay for it because she'd already eaten it by the time she got to the checkout line.

The second level of offenses were more serious. The extra five pounds on her hips because of overwrought ice-cream indulgences or not telling her mother the entire truth when she went parking with John Dewhurst when she was seventeen.

It was the third level that caused a serious lack of sleep. These were the true moral dilemmas where every solution was a painful one. There had been two of those: when her period was late five years ago, and Saturday night when she lied to Ben.

Thankfully, five years ago, her period had come three days after the fact, but she wasn't expecting the same of Ben.

She flopped on the couch, and studied her newly livable home.

He had done that for her.

The roof was intact, the floor polished and level, and

in her bedroom sat the brand-new Dreamscape Line Version I. Note to self: Must meet rail-thin boyfriend so he doesn't get poked in the back by bed. Someday she would part with that bed, perhaps burn it, but right now, the sadistic part of her wanted to keep it nearby.

She closed her eyes, practicing deep-breathing techniques, but in the end, she had saved herself a gargantuan heartbreak. Had he ever said he loved her? No. Had he ever talked about where their relationship was headed? No. Had he wanted to go pick out china? No.

Just when she was contemplating the housing options in Atlanta, the doorbell rang. All the possibilities ran through her head. Mailman, FedEx man, meter reader, Ben.

Instead, it was Mark. The old "this really isn't working out, even though it's been seven-years" dumper Mark. She blinked twice, thinking maybe it was her imagination, but each time she opened her eyes, there he was.

"Hi, Hilary." He raised his hand in greeting, somewhat sheepishly, but not nearly enough to dampen the surge of anger she felt. For that he would need to be down on his knees bearing gifts of gold and cool designer shoes.

Instead he stood there like a doofus, as though nothing had happened.

Unbelievable.

"What brings you to Texas? Seeing the sights?" she said, trying for a combination of ignorance and denial.

"I heard you were coming back to Atlanta."

There was an old saying, hell hath no fury like a woman scorned. Men didn't realize there was a lot of truth to that saying, Mark included.

The old Hilary would have slammed the door in his face. No, she would have read him the Riot Act, and then slammed the door in his face. The new, improved, I'm-in-control Hilary merely bit her tongue and said, "That is correct. Would you like some milk?"

She knew Mark hated milk, and he *knew* that she knew that he hated milk. But instead, she could pretend that she had forgotten all his preferences. Besides, no man got any ideas about reconciliation when being invited in for milk.

"Milk would be good," he said, obviously trying to earn huge brownie points.

He followed her inside and seated himself on the couch. She had vague couch memories with Mark, but she had Technicolor, stomach-clenching memories with Ben, and that made her smile.

Mark, ignorant of her thoughts, smiled back, which made her smile even wider.

"I'll get your milk," she said, heading for the kitchen.

As she reached into the refrigerator for her week-old milk carton, the doorbell rang again.

This time it was Ben.

12

HILARY FORGOT her manners, just stood there gaping like an idiot, but Ben didn't notice. Instead, he walked right in, coolly confident. She didn't like the idea that he was so sure of himself.

When he caught sight of Mark, Ben looked more uncertain, more nervous, and flat-out angry. Much better.

Then his faced cleared, all uncertainty disappeared, and he nodded to Mark. "My name's Ben."

Mark answered, extended his hand, but oddly enough, Ben didn't take it. Maybe Mark missed the significance of that, but Hilary didn't.

Ben waved carelessly. "Hilary, could I talk to you for a minute?"

His tone was bland, as if they were simply going to discuss the weather. That was unacceptable. "Uh, I have company."

"Should that be a factor? I'm sure Mark won't be offended."

Mark raised his hand. "I think I would."

Ben ignored him, as if he were of no consequence. As if the man that Hilary had nearly married was a bit of flotsam, not viable competition. "Hilary?"

That sort of dismissive attitude toward her life choices, possibly poor choices, but her choices notwithstanding, really tweaked her. She crossed her hands across her chest and tossed her hair, very Mae. "We can talk later."

The facade broke. There was some pain in his face now. It amazed her that she had the power to hurt him. "Don't do this," he said, almost pleading.

Mark chose the most inopportune time to butt in. "Now wait a minute, I think I have a say—"

Ben swung around, glaring at Mark. "Do you mind?"

And Mark didn't cower at all. "Yes, I do mind. I certainly do mind. I don't know who you are, or why you're here, but it's not important. What's important is that I want Hilary to come back home. Where she belongs."

Hilary mentally cheered as Mark stood his ground. He was a nice man, not the man of her dreams, but he wasn't pathetic. That meant she wasn't pathetic, either.

"And she belongs with you?" Ben asked.

Mark nodded, and Hilary felt even better. Ben took a long look at Hilary and she arched her brow.

If he wanted her, he was going to have to take a stand. That wasn't his strong suit, but she wasn't going to cave first.

"You think she belongs with you, then now's the time to prove it. Let's have a little pop quiz, shall we? I'll start with the beginning round. For one hundred points, question number one. What does Hilary do with her coffee?"

Mark's eyes narrowed and he looked confused. "Drink it."

Mark wasn't the only one confused. Hilary watched Ben carefully. What in the world was he doing?

"Bbzztt. I'm sorry. The correct answer is 'spill it.' Don't worry you still have time to catch up. Question two, for one hundred points. What does Hilary do when she's nervous?"

Mark rolled his eyes. "Twists her hair."

"Bbzztt. The correct answer is 'curl her toes.' Not doing so well, but don't give up yet, it's still early. For one hundred points, what is Hilary's favorite dance?"

Hilary stared down at her bare feet, at her toes scrunching and unscrunching. He had really noticed that? He had watched her toes? She looked back up at Ben, feeling a smile at the corners of her mouth.

Mark rocked back and forth on his feet. "Favorite dance? Two-step," he answered.

"Bbzztt. Tango. The correct answer is 'tango.' Down by three hundred. Not looking good, Mark, but we'll see how you do in the bonus round where the stakes are really high."

Hilary thought about interrupting, sparing Mark a little embarrassment, but now she wanted to see where this was going, and a little embarrassment would build up Mark's character nicely.

"Mark, this is for two hundred, true or false, Hilary is a good poker player."

"False."

"Bbzztt. The correct answer is 'true.' Last question, and this is for the game. Who loves Hilary?"

"I do."

Ben turned to Hilary and nodded. "That's right. The correct answer is 'I do.' So it looks like we have *a tie.*"

Hilary stared up at Ben, the man she'd thought was Mr. Above-the-Cut, Mr. I-Don't-Make-Time-with-Average-Women.

He loved her.

It was there in his eyes, and he was nervous. His hands were jammed in his pockets.

She had noticed that about him.

"You love me?"

"Yes."

Mark sat down on the couch. "I'm going to wait."

Still, Hilary felt she needed more convincing. "This isn't just because I dumped you?"

He frowned at her. "What?"

"Rejection. You know, suddenly I'm an unattainable quantity and have acquired a sort of mystique."

"I loved you before you dumped me. Dumping me did not improve your mystique."

"Do you think I have a mystique?"

"Do you want a mystique?"

Suddenly the world was open to her and anything

was possible. The impossible had suddenly become very possible. "Maybe not. You really love me?"

Ben sighed. "Why don't you believe me?"

Mark groaned. "I really don't want to hear this."

Hilary decided now was the time to tell him about her reality. He'd already glimpsed it before. "Because you haven't made the mistakes I have. *You* don't sit around waiting for life to happen to you, you're great-looking—" she took a good look at Mark, making sure he was listening "—so completely godlike in bed."

Ben caught on quick. "I do my best."

She winked at him. "Seven, eight times a night, it's more than any woman can ask for."

Mark got up from the couch. "I think I'm going to be sick. Hilary, I'm walking out the door and you can't stop me—"

"You're everything that I wanted in a man, a man who makes me scream with orgasmic ecstasy—"

"Oh, jeez. I'm opening the door."

"Who knows how to push every button inside my body—"

"The door is open. This is it. I'm going back to Atlanta." Hilary slammed the door shut behind Mark.

And then they were alone.

Ben loved her. My God, he really loved her.

He pulled her close, and she could see his heart in his eyes. "I love you, Hilary Sinclair."

For a moment she couldn't think, couldn't absorb the

truth, but then Mae came to her rescue. "And it's about time I realized it."

He kissed her until breathing became difficult, and when he raised his head, she was pleased to note that he was having difficulty as well.

"You know, I don't think you've ever screamed in orgasmic ecstasy."

Something like a purr escaped from her. She'd never purred before. She stared into the blue eyes that she was going to hold close every day of her life. "Well, that's a noble ambition."

"So, you're going to stay?" he asked.

"You really want me to?"

"Forever," he said, and sealed the promise with a single kiss. For a long time he held her close. "It's going to be good, Hilary."

She nearly cried. Such simple words, but they opened up a whole new life for her. With Ben. Would he ever realize how much she loved him? Maybe. After their ten-year anniversary. That was such a wonderful thought that she grinned. "I think screams of orgasmic ecstasy would be a step in the right direction. Why don't you start right now?"

He cocked his thumb toward her bedroom. "The Dreamscape Line Version I? I don't think so. You're coming to my place."

"Why?"

"Because I've got the Deluxe Dreamscape Line Version II."

And that did it. She locked her arms around his neck, completely Clingywoman. "I love you, Ben MacAllister."

As they walked out the door, he took a last look around. "So, you gonna keep this place?"

She took his arm and danced down the new improved front steps. "I'm glad you brought that up. I think I should add on a new room. Maybe a whirlpool bath. And the kitchen needs to be bigger..."

He took the hint and shut her up with his kiss. Quite nicely, in fact.

"MARY LYNN, I wanted to call you and apologize. I didn't think it was going to work, but you were right. It worked beautifully. He's taking over the company."

"And why did you doubt me, Martin?"

"You do know best. Want to buy a racehorse?"

"Martin MacAllister, you didn't!"

"Nah. Just joshing."

"Did you talk to Ben? I think our youngest will be getting married soon. He's talking about diamond rings. Something with an old-fashioned cut. I know Hilary will adore it."

"You think I'll have to wear a tuxedo again?"

"You are a selfish man."

"Not selfish, just don't like being uncomfortable. Maybe he could elope."

"If he wants you in a tuxedo, you wear a tuxedo."

"You going to bring a date?"

"Dr. Ludnecky asked me out for breakfast just yesterday."

"That old geezer?"

"Well, now if that ain't the pot calling the kettle black."

"Goodbye, Mary Lynn."

"I miss you, Martin."

"I could buy you coffee on Tuesday?"

"Busy on Tuesday."

"Wednesday?"

"That I can do."

Modern Romance™
...seduction and passion guaranteed

Tender Romance™
...love affairs that last a lifetime

Medical Romance™
...medical drama on the pulse

Historical Romance™
...rich, vivid and passionate

Sensual Romance™
...sassy, sexy and seductive

Blaze Romance™
...the temperature's rising

27 new titles every month.

Live the emotion

MILLS & BOON®

Live the emotion

Sensual Romance™

RED-HOT & RECKLESS by Tori Carrington
Nicole Bennett is a bad girl and an expert thief too! She's been in tight spots before but she has never been tailed by a guy like Alex Cassevetis! However, Nicole can't help thinking that getting into a tight spot with the sexy investigator might be a lot of fun…

MALE CALL by Heather MacAllister
When Marnie LaTour is told by the guy she's dating that she is not 'girlfriend material' she decides to take action! With a little help from the infamous 'man-magnet' skirt, she finds herself on a crash course to becoming the ultimate *femme fatale*…

SAY YOU WANT ME by Cindi Myers
Joni Montgomery needs a guy to pose as her boyfriend – and fast! When her blind date turns out to be gorgeous and willing, she thinks she's found the perfect man for the job. However, he is also a little *too* tempting for Joni to resist!

IN OVER HIS HEAD by Jacquie D'Alessandro
Lexie Webster needs a fling badly after her ex put her right off relationships. With her newest client Josh Maynard inspiring some *very* impure thoughts, Lexie becomes *determined* to seduce him – and he seems more than willing…

On sale 2nd April 2004

Available at most branches of WHSmith, Tesco, Martins, Borders, Eason, Sainsbury's and all good paperback bookshops.

0304/21

MILLS & BOON

EMMA DARCY

Kings *of the* Outback

THREE MASTERFUL BROTHERS — AND THE WOMEN WHO TAME THEM!

FREE
2 BOOKS
AND A SURPRISE GIFT!

We would like to take this opportunity to thank you for reading this Mills & Boon® book by offering you the chance to take TWO more specially selected titles from the Sensual Romance™ series absolutely FREE! We're also making this offer to introduce you to the benefits of the Reader Service™—

- ★ FREE home delivery
- ★ FREE monthly Newsletter
- ★ FREE gifts and competitions
- ★ Exclusive Reader Service discount
- ★ Books available before they're in the shops

Accepting these FREE books and gift places you under no obligation to buy; you may cancel at any time, even after receiving your free shipment. Simply complete your details below and return the entire page to the address below. *You don't even need a stamp!*

YES! Please send me 2 free Sensual Romance™ books and a surprise gift. I understand that unless you hear from me, I will receive 4 superb new titles every month for just £2.69 each, postage and packing free. I am under no obligation to purchase any books and may cancel my subscription at any time. The free books and gift will be mine to keep in any case.

T4ZEF

Ms/Mrs/Miss/Mr ....Initials ....
BLOCK CAPITALS PLEASE

Surname ....

Address ....

....

....Postcode ....

Send this whole page to:
UK: FREEPOST CN81, Croydon, CR9 3WZ
EIRE: PO Box 4546, Kilcock, County Kildare (stamp required)